The Source for

Augmentative

Alternative

Communication

Debra Reichert Hoge
Cheryl A. Newsome

Content Area: Augmentative and Alternative
Communication

Ages: 3 to Adult

LinguiSystems, Inc.
3100 4th Avenue
East Moline, IL 61244-9700
1-800-PRO IDEA
1-800-776-4332

FAX: 1-800-577-4555
E-mail: service@linguisystems.com
Web: www.linguisystems.com
TDD: 1-800-933-8331
(for those with hearing impairments)

About the Authors

Debra Reichert Hoge, Ed.D., CCC-SLP, is a professor in the Department of Special Education and Communication Disorders at Southern Illinois University Edwardsville. She teaches undergraduate and graduate courses in early intervention, child language development and disorders, low incidence populations, early childhood special education, and augmentative and alternative communication. Prior to becoming a faculty member at Southern Illinois, Debra taught in the public schools and at a center for autism. Debra has presented numerous workshops throughout the country on early intervention; assessment and intervention with infants, toddlers, and their families; syndromes; and early childhood special education issues. She was chosen as an author and presenter on two national in-service grants awarded to the American Speech-Language-Hearing Association (ASHA): ASHA's Building Blocks and ASHA's Interdisciplinary Preschool Project.

Debra is a native and a lifelong resident of St. Louis, Missouri and lives there with her husband, James, and daughter, Jillian Jean. *The Source for Augmentative and Alternative Communication* is Debra's third publication with LinguiSystems. She also co-authored *The Source for Syndromes* and *The Source for Syndromes 2*.

Cheryl A. Newsome, M.S., CCC-SLP, is Supervisor of Speech-Language Therapy Services for the Belleville Area Special Services Cooperative in Belleville, Illinois. In this capacity she provides technical support to speech-language pathologists (SLPs) in 23 school districts and serves as the SLP on the Augmentative Communication Evaluation and Support Team for the Cooperative. Cheryl's primary interest in the field of speech-language pathology involves children with autism, cerebral palsy, developmental delays, and other disorders that create difficulties with oral speech production. Before moving to Illinois, Cheryl was an SLP in Hawaii and Florida.

Cheryl has presented many workshops, primarily in the state of Illinois, for parents and professionals targeting functional communication strategies and early literacy skills. She has worked with the Illinois State Board of Education on task forces for establishing certification guidelines for school SLPs. Cheryl has also served on the Illinois Speech Hearing Association Representative Council from her area group in Southwestern Illinois (SWISHA). This is her first publication with LinguiSystems.

Edited by Barb Truman
Illustrations by Margaret Warner
Cover design by Mike Paustian
Page layout by Denise L. Kelly

Acknowledgments

Effective augmentative communication implementation depends on collaborative interactions. We are extremely thankful to the families, teachers, and staff who labor daily to provide more effective communication means and opportunities to our children through their daily interactions.

We especially need to recognize the contributions of three individuals who assisted in this project.

Mary Bettlach, MPH, OTR/L, our assistive technologist, who translated the verbiage of access into comprehensible terms for this book

Jami Bossart, MS, CCC-SLP, a dedicated speech-language pathologist in the school system who works tirelessly and creatively to implement communication through all available means for her students

Jamie Carney, MS, CFY, who researched websites and information for us to complete this text

We trust that your contributions to clients and this book have enlightened the present and will continue to illuminate the future.

Debbie and Cheryl

I am also grateful to my employer, Belleville Area Special Services Cooperative, and our director, Michael Blacharczyk, for their vision to serve children with augmentative communication needs and for the opportunities provided to me to lead this venture over the past ten years.

Cheryl

Dedications

This book would not have been possible without the exceptional support of our families. We would like to dedicate this book to our families:

Jim and Jillian Jean Hoge; Gene and Nita Reichert

and

Dick, Avalon, and Cheyenne Newsome; Bob and Hazel Parman

Table of Contents

Introduction

Intended Audience

This book is written for speech-language pathologists (SLPs) with persons on their caseloads who are nonverbal, or verbal but not highly intelligible. This would include speech-language pathologists involved in early intervention, schools, private practice, hospitals, and home health care. Audiologists and other adjunct professionals may also be interested in this information as services are often best provided by a transdisciplinary team.

The Source for Augmentative and Alternative Communication provides working professionals, preservice populations, and client families with a ready reference to information on rationale, assessment, and intervention procedures for the nonverbal population. There is an overabundance of information available concerning augmentative and alternative communication, but our goal is to provide the kinds of functional, useable, "what to do now," and "what to do next" kinds of facts and suggestions.

Specific populations with high percentages of augmentative users are addressed in detail so that this information is readily accessible when professionals are presented with clients carrying these diagnoses. Although many SLPs may have had some coursework in their preparatory programs, it is frequently heavy on theory and low on applicable methods and techniques. Many SLPs in training may not yet have had coursework or a client with augmentative communication needs. This text provides the needed specifics that SLPs and associated professionals can use in their daily work settings.

Historical Overview

The field and study of augmentative and alternative communication is not long steeped in history but rather is relatively new. Uses of augmentative and alternative communication strategies date back to the 1950s and 1960s with coursework and research emerging during the 1970s and continuing into the present. Four decades of development have led to great strides in the use of low-tech means as well as high-tech devices.

Advances made by the medical and scientific fields in the last five decades have created a need for augmentative and alternative communication. Many individuals who previously would have died due to illness, injury, neurological disease, or other causes are now surviving. Often these individuals can no longer communicate verbally, thus providing the impetus for the advancement of nonverbal means of communication. (A thorough discussion of the history of the development of augmentative and alternative communication can be found in Zangari et al. 1994.) From this initial movement following World War II (Lloyd, Fuller & Arvidson 1997) to the recent past and the passage of the Americans with Disability Act (ADA) (PL 101-336, 1990), our society has been made aware of the rights of persons with disabilities. One of these basic rights is to communicate.

Special education laws have also promoted the use of augmentative and alternative communicative means with children ages 3-21. The Education for All Handicapped Children Act (PL 94-142, 1975), which has been amended most recently as the Individuals with Disabilities Education Act Reauthorization Amendments of 1997 (PL 105-17, 1997), calls for the identification of children in need of alternative methods of communication as they begin to attend school. The provision of services to these children also includes their families and considers their needs for communication outside the school environment. According to today's standards of least restrictive environment, children who cannot speak or who speak too unintelligibly to be understood are placed in regular education with support for communication.

The American Speech-Language-Hearing Association (ASHA) has also developed guidelines for SLPs providing services to nonverbal populations. In a 1991 report, 13 roles and responsibilities for augmentative and alternative communication (AAC) professionals was published by ASHA and includes such duties as identifying possible candidates for AAC, evaluating, coordinating services, and consulting with family and allied personnel as well as the augmentative user (ASHA 1991). Another ASHA publication on the guidelines of meeting the communication needs of persons with severe disabilities was published in 1992 and contains a communication bill of rights (ASHA 1992). These rights include the right to request, to be offered choices, to protest, and to have access to any needed augmentative or alternative devices.

So as we enter into a new millennium, the focus on AAC continues to expand for SLPs and related professionals in a wide variety of work settings. *The Source for Augmentative and Alternative Communication* provides information on assessment for AAC, intervention strategies, teaming, and specifics on populations with a high percentage of augmentative users. You'll find lists of resources and contact information for companies making augmentative communication devices, as well as books, articles, and Web sites in the Appendixes. We hope you will find all you need for service provision within *The Source for Augmentative and Alternative Communication*.

Debbie and Cheryl

•8•

Preface

> I f my possessions were taken from me with one exception, I would choose to keep the power of communication, for by it, I would soon regain all the rest.
>
> —Daniel Webster

The gift of communication is one that is often taken for granted. Each day we communicate in a variety of ways for personal, social, and work-related matters. We communicate through touch, signals, gestures, and actions, as well as spoken and written words. Through communication, we gain information, weigh possibilities, and make decisions about all of our life activities. As we communicate, we display our values, our cognitive abilities, and our temperaments. Communication allows others not only to know about us but to actually know us.

When we seek to know someone better, we spend time listening and speaking with him to understand his thinking process and his perspective on the world. Through the individual's choice of words, topics, timing, and the balance between speaking and listening, we understand his life views and can gauge his interest in our views.

It is only when the gift is altered, taken away, or not given as part of the package that we begin to recognize the impact. Sensing the void in knowing the voiceless individual and his wishes leads us to the field of augmentative communication.

The world of augmentative communication is a relatively new field. Most speech-language pathologists (SLPs) practicing now have never had a course of study in augmentative communication, yet we are expected to be leaders of teams in this field as our professional responsibilities and diverse caseloads expand. For teachers and parents, there is an awareness that systems are "out there" and work for others, but the vastness of the technological field in which they operate and the number of choices and features available can be daunting. To begin this journey may feel like stepping off a cliff into a bottomless pit.

This book is meant to provide a stepping stone to the beginning of your knowledge of augmentative communication. As you begin down the path, it will feel like a cobblestone street, uneven and unsure, fraught with promise for movement and the possibility of tripping on the unsteady path at any time.

Perhaps rather than a journey on a cobblestone street, a path that has already been established, the journey for augmentative communication is instead more like an exploration. Each individual who is fitted with an augmentative communication device becomes part of the stored knowledge that is used in the next case you address. Building on confidence gained and learning from less effective measures, each subsequent augmentative communication matching experience becomes more art and less science. The intangibles you learn along the way combined with factual knowledge allow you to more effectively research feature matches for each successive client.

In this relatively new field of speech-language pathology, research is only beginning. Research is ongoing to determine the best combination of phrase-based and word-based utterances to meet the needs of communicators. Other areas of research include access modes and more efficient technology in smaller, lighter units to improve portability. As technology continues to advance with unprecedented speed, staying current may appear to be an impossible task.

Once you become involved in augmentative communication and experience the joy new communicators experience in their newfound ability to control their environment, keeping abreast of the technology and innovations in the field become challenges you are willing to accept. Confidence increases each time the team conducts an assessment and implements a device.

Writing a book about augmentative communication is risky business. We must address the methods and techniques used in assessment and implementation, but if we write about specific technologies, the book is outdated before the print is dry on the page. But, if you extract from this book principles to apply as you keep current with technology to match to a user, you have gained the basics that will guide you through whatever technology may follow.

As experience builds, you begin to have a "feel" for technologies that will work for particular individuals. For example, you see new features in technologies and immediately a particular user or situation comes to mind. When these kinds of connections become reality for you, both you and your clients benefit.

As technology changes to make access and vocabulary easier for the user, our job as the support team must be to continue to foster independence and encourage the user to achieve his potential in all arenas. It is not until we expect the best of others that they can demonstrate to us what and who they are, and who they can truly become.

In this field of practice, as in all others, some days will be better than others. Some days all of the pieces fit, all of the batteries stay charged, and no device simply fails to work. On other days, it appears that problems are raining down around us in buckets. Regardless of the kind of day it is, we encourage you to keep your chin up, correct what you can, and move on. Dedicating yourself to helping others communicate who they are and who they want to become is a noble venture. Enjoy each day.

> **F**inish each day and be done with it. You have done what you could. Some blunders and absurdities, no doubt, crept in. Forget them as soon as you can. Tomorrow is a new day. You will begin it well and serenely.
>
> —Ralph Waldo Emerson

What Is Augmentative and Alternative Communication?

1

Definitions

Augmentative and alternative communication (AAC) is often considered a subset of "assistive technology." *Assistive technology* is defined by the Tech Act (PL 100-407, 1988) as "any item, piece of equipment, or product system, whether acquired commercially, off the shelf, modified, or customized, that is used to increase, maintain, or improve the functional capabilities of individuals with disabilities." *Augmentative communication,* as explained by King (1999), is a subset of assistive technology that deals with support and/or replacement of natural speaking, writing, and other communication capabilities that do not fully meet the communicator's needs. *AAC* then is an inclusive term for any system that facilitates communication with techniques, strategies, equipment, or other resources to support an individual's expressive communication.

Not all AAC systems include high-tech or high-priced solutions to support the communication of challenged speakers. Basic types of systems are described in the following pages as "high tech" or "low tech," but in reality, there are often no clear demarcations between these systems. What is new and relatively "high tech" today will be eclipsed by the technology of the future. For example, few of us consider handheld calculators as "high tech," yet they were not commonly available 30-40 years ago. Another familiar trend is that the cost of items declines as the items gain market share and the technology is used in a wider variety of equipment. Handheld calculators with fewer capabilities than our current models originally sold for more than $200 when they were first introduced.

Types of Systems

Some examples of traditional systems include sign language and gestures, Bliss symbols, picture point systems, and choice making (i.e., selecting between actual items or representations of them). Current systems run a wide gamut from low-tech systems without voice output to high-tech systems with multiple-voice selections and fully customized vocabulary systems.

- non-speaking systems
- low-tech voice-output systems
- high-tech voice-output systems

Non-Speaking Systems

- object systems
- natural gestures
- sign language
- pictographic symbol systems
- eye-gaze/blink systems

Object Systems

Often one of the first pairings is to associate objects with desired outcomes. Even infants who learn the association between hunger and the bottle will begin to calm when they understand that their message has been received and someone is about to address their needs. Likewise, first requests and communications can be accomplished by using actual objects (touching the milk carton for a drink), objects that are associated with an activity (touching one's hat to go outside), or miniature objects (a toy computer for access to the real thing). This level is one of the early symbolic representational systems for communication.

Natural Gestures

Although the first inclination for an individual who lacks voice output may be to provide an audible "voice" for communication, voice output is not always required or advantageous for the user. There are highly effective communication systems for some users that do not require voice output.

One such system involves the use of natural gestures. Many times caregivers will report that non-speaking individuals communicate with them through various means (e.g., looking at what they want, facial expressions) (Silverman 1989, Beukelman & Mirenda 1998). An extension of this type of communication is to reinforce and teach natural gestures, such as reaching, pointing, shaking and nodding of the head or smiling to reinforce a communication partner's statement. Although some individuals will develop these systems spontaneously, some will not. The individuals who do not learn to use natural gestures independently may still be candidates for gestural communication with intervention. (See Chapter 5 for programming ideas.)

Natural gestures have the positive trait of always being available to the user, typically understood by others, and efficient in their transmission. Selecting a natural gesture system does not preclude the use of other systems for other functions, or pairing gestures with another system (e.g., use of voice to gain attention prior to gesturing for communication). One specific limitation to consider is the individual's ability to control gross and fine motor movements to produce gestures that others can understand.

Sign Language

Another nonverbal system of communication is sign language. For some individuals, sign language is an appropriate means of communication. They may be hearing impaired and highly involved in the deaf community, or work or live in a facility that relies on gestures and sign language as the primary communication system.

There are several signing systems available. Some are based on fingerspelling, in which a hand position stands for each letter of the alphabet. American Sign Language (AMSLAN) is one of these systems and is the one used by interpreters for the deaf. Another system based on fingerspelling is Signing Exact English (SEE), but SEE also incorporates morphological markers and is used with populations learning syntactical markers.

Many signs are iconic (i.e., they resemble the action or word that they represent); therefore sign language may be a natural extension of a gesture-based system. However, sign language is by no means universally understood in the general population. Since some individuals may not have the fine motor capabilities to produce exact signs, the signs may be adapted. As long as the interactive partners in the signer's environment understand the signs, communication can occur.

One advantage of sign language is that the system (hands) is always available for communication. Another advantage is that sign can be used with concurrent speech as an input system. Signing while speaking to a student provides two modes with which to take in information. Further strategies to address this two-way communication idea are explored in Chapter 5.

The greatest disadvantage to the system is that it is often not read and recognized by the community at large, especially with unfamiliar communication partners. Populations with which to consider signing would include persons with hearing loss, persons with cognitive impairment, persons with brain damage or cerebral palsy, and children with developmental apraxia.

Pictographic Symbol Systems

Several pictographic symbol systems have been developed to assist in communication for those unable to speak. Some systems are based on the belief that there is a hierarchy of symbol recognition moving from concrete to more abstract. Some students follow this arrangement from realistic pictures (photographs) to less sophisticated black-and-white pictures, and then to line drawing representations. Other students will understand line drawings and be confused or unresponsive to more

- Bliss symbols
- Minspeak systems
- Rebus symbols
- Picsyms
- Picture Communication Symbols
- Morse code
- Picture exchange systems

detailed or colorful pictures. The individual user's preferences, visual acuity, and visual processing of information are essential elements to consider when determining the type of pictures appropriate for a communication system.

Other considerations when developing a pictorial system include size of pictures, location of pictures on display, number of pictures presented, color versus black-and-white pictures, and other individual preferences. Picture systems vary considerably in their complexity and cognitive requirements of the user. The systems outlined below are only a sampling of these types of systems.

- **Bliss Symbols**

  Bliss symbols were developed in 1965 by Charles Bliss to function as an auxiliary language for written international communication (Silverman 1989). Single elements can be used alone or modified and manipulated to create a different or more specific meaning for a picture symbol. This system can require more representational understanding and awareness of language form and content if used at the most sophisticated levels. When used in tandem with voice-output systems, Bliss symbols can represent abstract and complex referents.

- **Minspeak Systems**

  The Minspeak system was devised in 1982 by Bruce Baker as a semantic compaction system. The idea was to access a wide variety of words with a set of static pictures and categories based on features in those systems. Using picture representations for groups of items (e.g., apple for all foods), choices can then be selected that further define the food item (apple + cactus = Mexican food items; apple + cactus + sunrise = taco). A variety of versions of the picture symbol associations from simple to complex is available to address cognitive and developmental levels.

- **Rebus Symbols**

  Another pictographic symbol set originally used for building reading and language development skills is rebus symbols (Blackstone 1986). Rebus symbols are often used as a visual support for a word or syllable. For example, the rebus picture of a tied rope may indicate "not" or "knot." The most common rebus collection used to support reading and communication both in the United States and in the United Kingdom includes more than 3,500 rebuses (Beukelman & Mirenda 1998).

- **Picsyms**

  Picsyms is another line drawing symbol system based on a set of consistent principles to generate messages (Carlson 1985, Beukelman & Mirenda 1998). With a library of 880 line drawings, new Picsyms can be generated by following the rule system designated by their training materials. Faith Carlson, the inventor of Picsyms, later created Dynasyms as a computer format of Picsyms for use with augmentative communication devices in the Dynavox family of devices.

·14·

- **Picture Communication Symbols**

Another series of line drawing picture symbols used for communication is the Picture Communication Symbols (PCS) (Johnson 1994). This system is available in a variety of formats, including written books (ready for photocopying). The Boardmaker computer program allows any of the over 3,000 PCS symbols to be printed in a size determined by the user in either black-and-white or color. Pre-made grids for common augmentative communication devices are furnished with this software program. Other grids can be easily designed using the on-screen rulers. The ease of use and speed of this program to create classroom communication materials has increased its popularity among busy teachers and clinicians. Many of the line drawings of more difficult to picture concepts rely on the signed vocabulary for their representation.

finished   help

The Picture Communication Symbols © 1981-2002 Mayer-Johnson, Inc. Used with permission.

Numerous other picture symbols have been produced in this country and others for use with non-speaking individuals. The difficulty with any picture system lies in providing the user access to enough pictures to convey routine messages as well as to represent ideas or words that are novel. Picture systems may prove a very useful tool for beginning communicators, but complex, rule-generated systems often require a heavy cognitive load.

- **Morse Code**

The system of dots and dashes that first earned notoriety as the communication system of the telegraph is a viable option for some communicators. Morse code can be "read" with or without an electronic linkage if the receiver is proficient in this language and understands the transmission system of the sender. Morse code can be used as an input system as well as a component of a more complex communication system. Morse code is dependent on the user knowing how to spell, but it can be accomplished with the smallest of movements to convey messages (Silverman 1989, King 1999).

- **Picture Exchange Systems**

Picture communication systems have been present in the field for many years, but recently they have seen renewed interest. Frost and Bondy (1994) have studied pictures as a way for children with autism to communicate effectively with others in their environment. Their system, the Picture Exchange Communication System, pairs the use of pictures with a highly structured behavioral system for interactions. They begin by teaching the child to ask for highly reinforcing items using a picture that functions as a "ticket." The first goal is to understand that use of the picture causes something desirable to occur. After the communication exchange is established, the focus shifts to picture discrimination (selecting the correct picture for the item desired). Higher levels of communication are also outlined in this system.

In the young children Bondy and Frost studied in the Delaware Autism Project, some children developed speech as they attempted to develop this system of functional communication. Verbal speech was the byproduct of this augmentative system, not the goal. Since this system was introduced, applications have been attempted with students with communication problems other than autism.

The methods for increasing the complexity of utterances for students with apraxia or developmental disabilities vary from those in students with autism. Looking at typical language development at the two-word stage, Rouse and Katera (2000) have adapted the developmental language learning stages into picture associations. For example, instead of adding "I want" as the second picture with a noun, Rouse and Katera recommend using two picture combinations that change the pragmatic function or semantics of the word combinations (e.g., noun + action; noun + more).

Eye-Gaze/Blink Systems

One extension of natural gestures to obtain desired objects is use of an eye-gaze system. Eye gaze can now be used as an input system as well as an independent low-tech system. Eye-gaze communication systems use clear plastic or plexiglass boards called ETRAN systems to designate specific locations for picture communications. The communication partner is able to determine where the user is focusing and reinforce the communication exchange.

Eye-blink systems of communication involve blinking a set number of times for a limited number of basic messages (Silverman 1989). The system may involve one blink for a "yes" answer and two blinks for "no." Again, both of these systems require that the receiver understand the sender's system for the communication to be effective.

Low-Tech Voice-Output Systems

Recorded Single-Message Systems

A variety of low-tech systems are available for beginning communicators or for use in special circumstances. Such systems include handheld recording toys (e.g., Yak Bak), talking picture frames, and personal dictation devices—all of which can be purchased at toy stores or electronic stores.

Single-message switches are also available from manufacturers of augmentative and assistive technology (e.g., Big Mack switch, loop tape systems). Often these same switches can be used for input into another device (e.g., a computer or environmental control unit) to control some other aspect of an exchange. Single-message switches allow you to record a "live voice" (digitized) message that is played back when the user activates the switch or button. Single-message switches

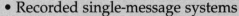

- Recorded single-message systems
- Recorded magnetic strip cards
- Multi location voice output devices
- Voice-amplification systems
- Text-to-speech systems

are portable, easy to program, and easily changed to accommodate a number of situations throughout a day. These switches can be a boost to beginning literacy activities as outlined in Chapter 5.

Durability of these switches depends on the materials and workmanship that varies across manufacturers. Typically, switch manufacturers for students with special needs understand that durability is imperative. Toys and business aids are not meant for the same level of use as an everyday single-switch user.

Single switches can be used for greetings by beginning communicators to initiate a communication. If you are attempting to teach beginning cause and effect, a single switch that requests a desired reinforcer ("Please rub my back.") can prove to be a powerful teaching tool. Other uses include calling for attention or assistance if no vocal means is available, or programming in a repeated phrase ("Chicka Chicka Boom Boom") from a story to allow the nonverbal child to participate in story time.

Recorded Magnetic-Strip Cards

An old technology that has found a new function in augmentative communication is the use of Language Master cards for communication. Either words or pictures can be placed on the card with the magnetic strip. Once the message is recorded on the card, it can be played by feeding the card into the reader on the machine and the digitized voice message is received. This system may be particularly helpful for teaching specific skills in the classroom setting.

Multiple-Location Voice-Output Devices

Low-tech multiple-location voice-output devices can range in size from two to 40 locations on a static overlay. A *static overlay* is described as a set of words or pictures that does not change. Generally using recorded (digitized) speech, these devices allow a greater selection of choices than single-message voice-output devices. Each location is coded with a word, picture, or both that identifies the message to be spoken when that location is selected. Simple devices in this category are accessed by touching the desired picture, but more complex systems use scanning systems for communicators who cannot select the location due to fine motor limitations. Messages stored can be single words, phrases, or sentences. The length of message is dictated by the number of messages and total recording time provided by the manufacturer on each particular device. Many SLPs may know the Language Master and its restricted opportunity for recording. Other examples would include devices with from four to 32 locations with recording times that vary from 30 seconds to 45 minutes.

Some of these devices allow for multiple overlays or levels. These levels can be changed to provide a completely new set of messages to be used in a different environment. Often up to four or more sets of vocabulary can be stored and easily retrieved. The manufacturer provides specific directions for changing the vocabulary sets on their devices. Generally, however, the process would be to change the laminated overlay (picture set) and select the corresponding vocabulary set using the switch on the device. For many users, this static overlay is less challenging than more complex methods of retrieving vocabulary that we will explore under high-tech devices, pages 20-22.

Voice-Amplification Systems

If an individual has the ability to generate speech but lacks vocal intensity to project her voice adequately to engage in conversations, one option is a personal voice-amplification system. Functioning much as a traditional microphone system, the microphone is small and fitted for the user. The amplification system can be a small speaker attached to the user's wheelchair or worn around the waist. Current models require a cord from speaker to microphone. Future systems will undoubtedly offer a wireless version.

Some voice-amplification systems modulate the transmission frequencies of individuals with dysarthric speech to enhance the intelligibility of their speech. Currently these systems require an evaluation by a trained representative in order to use them for a trial period. One example of this system is the Speech Enhancer System, which is manufactured by Electronic Speech Enhancement, Inc. (See Appendix A, page 127.)

Text-to-Speech Systems

Text-to-speech systems may be loaded onto computers or can be individual units used for communication. Self-contained systems are typically no larger than a standard keyboard and are light and portable. These systems allow the user to generate novel utterances provided they have the fine motor and spelling abilities to use the system.

Up to three lines of text may be visible in the display window, allowing the user to construct a message before presenting it. Some systems have several files that allow the user to prepare and store text that is commonly used (as for everyday conversations) or to prepare for a specific event, such as a doctor's visit. Messages can be spoken letter by letter, word by word, line by line, sentence by sentence, or paragraph by paragraph, depending on settings adjusted by the user. Synthesized speech is used. Some adjustments to pronunciation can be made through the dictionary menu, which "remembers" the preferred pronunciations. For example, if the word "read" is programmed as the past tense verb ("red"), then it would not be produced as "reed" in the present-tense verb opportunities.

Files written on this device can be downloaded to a printer if the cable is attached to the printer port, allowing for written communication as well as verbal communication. Text can also be transferred to a computer for use in another environment or as an addition to an already existing document.

Text-to-speech systems may also have the capability to generate word prediction. (See the example below.) In this software, the user selects the first letter of the desired word, and when it is entered, the system presents an optional word list beginning with that letter. If the targeted word appears, the user need only select the numbered option and the entire word with a space following it is transferred into the text of the message without additional keystrokes.

```
O
1: On       2: Of       3: One      4: Once     5: Or

Once u
1: up       2: upon     3: until    4: ugly     5: used

Once upon a time t
1: they     2: there    3: this     4: then     5: these

Once upon a time there was a l
1: lot      2: lunch    3: letter   4: light    5: line

Once upon a time there was a la
1: lake     2: late     3: later    4: law      5: lady

Once upon a time there was a lar
1: large    2: larger
```

Features of word prediction systems may vary. Some use the memory of selected words as a frequency base to predict what word the user may want next. So if a typical user opens conversations with "How are you today?" the system will begin to generate "how" as one of the first options when the letter "h" is entered.

Other word prediction systems may have grammatical prediction capabilities. Based on previous experience with the user and the software knowledge of what follows, these devices will generate a guess of what word the user may want before the first letter of the next word is entered. For example, if "I" is entered as the first choice, what follows is a list of verbs (e.g., *am, feel, want, will*) for the user to select from prior to entering a first letter. If the desired word is in that option list, the user need only select it and a new list of possible "next words" is generated.

For users who have spelling and reading difficulties, some systems will highlight and read the word choices to allow the user to select the correct word from the auditory scan. Word prediction capabilities are often part of higher technology augmentative communication systems and are an important consideration for individuals with reduced speed in input selections due to motoric limitations.

Features

- Static or dynamic display
- Digitized or synthesized speech output
- Direct and/or indirect access modes

High-Tech Voice-Output Systems

High-tech systems feature a seemingly endless array of features and options in a single, self-contained unit. These systems are often significantly more expensive than low-tech systems, and therefore evaluation teams often feel pressured to select the "perfect" system that will allow a communicator to be successful at this time, as well as allow for communication growth within the system. In order to make the best decision, the team needs to match evaluation results, product features, and communication environments. Knowing and understanding the features is the beginning of the matching process.

Static or Dynamic Display

Static display screens have a set number of locations and pictures that remain on the device at all times. Some devices may allow you to set a variety of static displays, but the choice is limited by the number of locations the device can accept. High-tech static display locations can range from 40-128, depending on the device. Some devices allow you to "link" one choice to another to create a greater variety of messages from a static overlay. Examples of these types of systems include Minspeak by Prentke Romich and the DynaSyms by Dynavox. These strategies are further discussed in Chapter 5.

Dynamic screen devices function much as a screen at an automatic teller machine at a bank. Examples of these devices would include the Dynavox, Portable Impact, Vanguard, and Pathfinder systems. Once you select an item from the first available menu, the menu changes to allow you to follow a "path" to find the choice you want. Dynamic screens that function under this same principle often allow you to customize the size and location of choices on the screen. A dynamic screen allows arrangement of vocabulary and choices to be customized to a system the user understands.

Digitized or Synthesized Speech Output

Most high-tech augmentative communication devices use synthesized (computer) speech for voice output. The voice can typically be adjusted to reflect the user (e.g., male, female, age, pitch, rate). Many systems also allow for the addition of digitized (recorded live voice) speech output, which may allow you to record a spoken message or a particular song or recorded passage that has special importance to the user.

Access Modes

• **Direct Access**

Most high-tech communication devices allow a variety of methods to activate them and select the message to be communicated. Generally, the easiest and quickest for many individuals is direct selection. For lower technology options, direct communication may be forming the sign language representation, exchanging the picture, or pointing to the picture or object that you want.

For electronic devices, direct selection gives the user the ability to choose from all available symbol choices at any given time (Glennen & DeCoste 1997). Direct selection may include activating the device with your finger, a pointer, an infrared beam, or other adaptation to activate a symbol choice. For individuals capable of accurately targeting locations, direct selection is the most efficient method of communication with an augmentative device.

• **Indirect Access**

For many individuals, direct selection is not possible due to limits in fine motor planning and control. The defining difference between direct and indirect access is timing. Direct access allows individuals to select any item at any time from the array of choices presented. Indirect access uses scanning and therefore adds extra time to the communication initiation and/or response.

In scanning, the device is programmed to highlight selections on the screen in a particular sequence. When the target message is highlighted, the user selects the location to communicate the message. A number of scanning types, arrangements, and speeds are typically included in high-tech systems and may be essential for augmentative communication users with physical challenges.

Scanning strategies may include row/column, linear, or step scanning. Scanning involves the additional cognitive skill of waiting for the correct location to activate and timing the activation. There may be more than one activation required to access a selected location.

For example, row/column scanning allows faster access to a large group of icons than scanning each button on a 32-location device. (See the example on the next page.) If the location the user wishes to activate is located in position "O" as identified on the following page, the device would begin by scanning row one, then go to row two. When row two is highlighted, the user activates his switch. The device begins to scan across the icons on this row, and when the fourth item is highlighted, the user again activates his switch to select that icon.

On systems with large static overlays, scanning by quadrants may be an option. The scanning process does require significantly more time than direct-selection methods.

Other scanning alternatives include the following:

- *Linear scanning*—usually a left to right or circular scanning pattern used with four to eight location devices

- *Step scanning*—requires the user to activate his switch to move the scan process. When he stops activating his switch, it selects the icon where the step scanning stopped. This type of scanning can be used in conjunction with either a row/column or linear scanning arrangement.

The use of scanning requires an input system of a switch to indicate the selection (choice). The user can employ almost any movement that is voluntary and controllable to activate the switch, so a variety of switch types and positions can be considered.

Factors to consider when selecting a switch include what intentional and consistent movement the individual can produce, the size or timing of the movement, the feedback (e.g., clicks or visual or tactile sensations) needed for the user, and the positioning of the switch/input device. Considerations must also include other issues of a medical nature (e.g., access to ventilators, access in and out of the wheelchair, mobility of the wheelchair) and the appearance of the switch to the user. Any sensory or tactile issues that affect the user must also be addressed. More information on matching movements, switches, and users is found in Chapter 4.

Conclusion

With the wide variety of communication systems available and technology always moving forward, it may seem that making the choice of the perfect communication system is an impossible dream. As new systems arrive on the market at unprecedented speed, selecting the device itself can be a daunting task.

Later material on assessment and intervention demonstrates that selecting the device is not the first task, nor the most important. Instead, being aware of options and matching them to the needs identified in assessment and situations described in Chapter 5, are what ensures success for the communication process.

Special Populations 2

Certain populations have a particularly high percentage of nonverbal or minimally verbal members. These individuals may benefit from augmentative or alternative communicative means. Many of these populations manifest a congenital or acquired disorder or pathology of the central nervous system, and some may have an unknown etiology for their lack of intelligible speech. This chapter addresses the populations listed below and outlines specific augmentative communication considerations for each.

- cerebral palsy
- apraxia
- hearing impairment
- deaf-blind
- autism
- developmental disabilities
- Down syndrome
- dysarthria
- acquired disorders

Cerebral Palsy

Cerebral palsy can be thought of as a paralysis, weakness, or lack of sensation in an area of the body that is caused by some type of brain injury or lack of brain development during the prenatal, perinatal, or very early postnatal periods of development. Cerebral palsy is a nonprogressive disorder, sometimes referred to as *static encephalopathy*, and is highly individualized in its presentation. There are various types of cerebral palsy, the most common of which are spastic, athetoid, and ataxic. Some individuals also present with mixed-type cerebral palsy.

Spastic cerebral palsy involves the simultaneous overcontraction of muscle groups, presenting as hypertonicity in selected body parts. Flailing, nonpurposeful movement of body parts characterizes the athetoid type of cerebral palsy. Ataxic cerebral palsy is exhibited by balance difficulties.

Each of these types of cerebral palsy can affect any or all parts of the body: upper and/or lower extremities as well as the speech producing mechanisms. Terms such as *quadriplegia* (four appendages), *hemiplegia* (right or left half), and *paraplegia* describe which parts of the body are affected by the cerebral palsy, and *spastic quadriplegia* describes both the type of cerebral palsy and the part of the body affected. Knowing both the type and the location of the disability helps the clinician anticipate challenges the individual with cerebral palsy might have.

One important consideration in working with clients with cerebral palsy is a team approach that includes a physical therapist and an occupational therapist. Cerebral palsy is primarily a motor disorder and you must have an assessment of the patient's motor functioning before considering an augmentative means of communication. Seating and positioning for augmentative use are essential considerations as well as fine and gross motor planning abilities and control. Range of motion, strength, endurance, and speed of movement should also be taken into account. Wide variations of motor challenges are found in this population. These patients may move from one piece of positioning equipment to another (e.g., standing box, sidelyer, wheelchair, beanbag, tumbleforms) and the communication needs for the individual in each position should be evaluated and considered.

Disorders Associated with Cerebral Palsy

- communication difficulties
- visual disabilities
- hearing loss
- dual sensory impairment
- seizures
- developmental delay
- gross/fine motor challenges

Communication disorders associated with cerebral palsy can result from nervous system involvement affecting respiratory, laryngeal, pharyngeal, and/or oral and nasal articulatory systems. Dysarthria and apraxia may also be present with weakness, paralysis, or lack of sensation in various areas. Due to the wide range of difficulties with oral speech in this population, persons with cerebral palsy are some of the earliest documented clients to use augmentative means of communication.

Cerebral palsy is also associated with other disorders, such as cognitive challenges, visual disabilities, hearing loss, seizure disorders, and developmental disabilities. When hearing loss is combined with visual difficulties, the child has a dual sensory impairment. Presence of associated disabilities require input from additional team members (e.g., physical therapist, occupational therapist, vision specialist, audiologist) when considering an augmentative communication system.

·24·

Assessing functional cognitive level allows the team to consider what types of symbols the individual might be able to use, ranging from very concrete to abstract. Visual differences can also play a major role in symbol system selection with this population. Visual acuity, visual field deficits, and visual perceptual abilities must all be determined per individual. The size and composition of the individual's assessment and implementation team for augmentative communication increases with the severity and breadth of the areas of concern or delay.

A wide variety of communication systems may be used with this population. Some types of augmentative communication include adaptive sign and low-tech means as well as high-tech electronic devices. In many cases, the use of more than one modality facilitates communication.

Apraxia

Apraxia can be developmental and detected in the preschool years or acquired as a result of a brain lesion as in a traumatic brain injury or a cerebrovascular accident. This disorder is neurologically based and affects only the programming for speech sound production. This difficulty in motor planning and production can result in unintelligible speech production. The speech errors produced tend to be of an inconsistent nature and speech is likely to become more unintelligible with longer utterances. Omissions and sound substitutions are the most usual speech errors found in apraxia.

Due to the high levels of unintelligibility, patients with apraxia may benefit from the use of an augmentative communication system. Often there are few, if any, other areas of concern for an individual with developmental apraxia, so the transdisciplinary team may be small. As long as receptive language skills are age appropriate, children with apraxia can be fully included in the

Other Names for Apraxia

• developmental apraxia of speech (DAS)

• oral apraxia

• verbal apraxia

• dyspraxia

regular educational setting. In this case, preschool and elementary teachers would be included on the team. In addition, since these individuals may also be some of the youngest clients we see with apraxia, the family must be included as members of the team. Parental counseling may also fall to the team as this child's speech disorder may be severe to profound.

For the highly unintelligible child with apraxia, early use of multimodal approaches including augmentative communication allows the child the opportunity to use language from a very early age. If a team "waits" for intelligible speech to develop, precious language learning time may be wasted. Aided and unaided means, such as natural speech, gestures, signs, and voice-output systems, may be combined for the best interactional opportunities.

Since the majority of these children are ambulatory, portable devices and means should also be considered.

Intelligence is generally in the normal range for this population, so picture communication books may be too limiting. A large numbers of words/pictures would need to be included to keep pace with a child's rapidly developing vocabulary. Instead, multiple overlays or dynamic screen capabilities for a voice-output system are essential. Mini-communication books or topic books or boards may also be used in particular settings with the specific vocabulary needed for that activity.

Supporting the child's attempts to communicate in a true augmentative role would be the primary goal for team intervention. However, the child with developmental apraxia may also have disorders in the areas of reading, writing, and spelling, so these supplemental language areas should be addressed. Other populations (e.g., children with mental retardation, autism, and cerebral palsy) are also known to have increased incidences of apraxia and warrant a thorough assessment.

Acquired apraxia that is found in populations such as persons with traumatic brain injury and stroke, presents itself with the same types of speech sound errors as found in developmental apraxia of speech. Differences, however, are that the patients with acquired apraxia may also have associated disorders. Depending on the location and severity of the neurologic insult, language problems may exist due to decreased cognitive and memory skills. When considering augmentative communication for an individual with acquired apraxia, the hospital-based team members would typically lead the evaluation and implementation process. As with developmental apraxia, a wide variety of technology may meet the patient's communication needs in specific situations, depending upon the lifestyle demands.

Hearing Impairment

Children identified with hearing loss are some of the first to use augmentative and alternative methods of communication. Signing systems have been used for many years with children who are deaf or hard of hearing.

Hearing loss can be of a permanent or fluctuating nature and can be conductive, sensorineural, or both. It can run the gamut from mild to severe and can affect one or both ears. Hearing can be lost after the development of language or a hearing loss may be present from birth, thus interfering with typical language development. Causes for hearing impairment include prenatal, developmental, and acquired conditions. Early diagnosis and intervention are imperative in this population and a thorough evaluation of the specific hearing skills the individual possesses provides essential information to the AAC team. Some potential AAC users may have undetermined auditory status, and in that case, Blischak and Wasson (1997) suggest proceeding as if the person has a hearing impairment.

·26·

Provide auditory training, amplification, adaptations to communication, and audiological monitoring if their behavior suggests difficulty in understanding speech.

The individual with a hearing impairment may require amplification from a hearing aid, cochlear implant, and/or another assistive listening device. All existing modes of communication should be used, and may include visual, manual, and auditory. Receptive and expressive communication abilities should be considered, as each individual presents a unique profile. Natural gestures, signing, and systems using written symbol input and output are some of the augmentative choices to support reception of language input as well as a system for expression. Reading and writing abilities may also benefit from the use of an augmentative system.

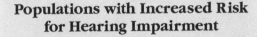

Populations with Increased Risk for Hearing Impairment

- autism
- cerebral palsy
- mental retardation
- head trauma
- developmental disability
  (Lloyd, Fuller & Arvidson 1997)

Paul (2001) suggests a Total Communication system for children with severe hearing impairment who are at the emerging-language stage. The earliest symbolic aspects of language can be introduced to children with hearing impairment through total communication as semantic relations are developing. Combining signs to express the relationships comes as a second level of instruction. The augmentative communicative means for this population can range from low-tech to very high-tech. Appropriate use of assistive technology and monitoring of equipment function on a daily basis will help the person with hearing impairment optimize communicative interactions.

Deaf-Blind

Deficits in both hearing and vision in children who are deaf-blind may be due to Fetal Rubella syndrome or Usher's syndrome. These children almost always benefit from augmentative communication. Gestures, adapted signs, finger spelling, and print or Braille systems can increase communication as well as tactile communication boards, symbol systems, teletouch devices, and computers.

Autism

Autism is a disorder that was first identified in 1943 by Dr. Leo Kanner following his observation of persons he considered to be concerned only with "self." The term *autism* comes from the root *auto* meaning "self." Dr. Kanner found the people in his study fascinating in terms of their social and communicative behaviors. Although the definition of autism has changed throughout the last fifty-plus years, social and communicative differences remain at the heart of the disorder.

Autism is considered to be one of the Pervasive Developmental Disorders (American Psychiatric Association 1994) and currently has a differential diagnosis setting it apart from other pervasive developmental disorders. Delays or abnormal functioning in social development, play, and language used for social communication must be reported prior to age three to meet the diagnostic criteria of autism according to the Diagnostic and Statistical Manual of Mental Disorders (DSM-IV) (American Psychiatric Association 1994).

The team approach is essential in considering augmentative communication for individuals with autism. The co-occurring difficulties in cognition, language development, sensory system differences, mental rigidity, stereotypic behaviors, and reciprocal social interaction all require intense collaboration of professionals and family members. Occupational therapists, early interventionists, educators, audiologists, speech-language pathologists, behavior consultants, and medical professionals all have viable views as to the needs of the individual.

A significant percentage of this population remains nonverbal with apraxia as a possible causation factor. Those who are verbal often exhibit atypical paralinguistic aspects of communication, such as monotonous intonation, loudness differences, and unusual stress patterns.

Cognitive functioning in this population is difficult to assess due to the profound communicative and social impairments, and often due to sensory differences. On standardized measures, individuals may score along a spectrum from gifted to severe/profound retardation. The cause for autism is currently unknown, although brain differences in individuals with autism have been found with PET scans and MRI technology. Some newer trends of thought are emerging from more current research. One possibility in some cases is that there is a genetic link (Richard & Hoge 1999).

Atypical behaviors are one of the first signs of autism. Self-stimulatory movements, ritualistic behaviors, non-interactive behaviors, and tantrum behaviors even as toddlers can be evident. These behaviors often interfere with communicative training and should be taken into account as the assessment team considers augmentative communication means.

Sensory system differences can range from hyposensitivity to hypersensitivity in any of the sensory areas: auditory, visual, olfactory, taste, tactile, vestibular, or proprioceptive. Any of the sensory perceptions may be targeted in an individual's self-stimulatory behaviors. Sensory integration therapies, under the direction of specially trained occupational therapists, may help some children better regulate their sensory systems. These sensory reactions must be taken into account when considering an augmentative means of communication.

A current thought is that individuals with autism have strengths in the visual realm and that this sensory system may be a beneficial avenue for training individuals with autism. Temple Grandin, an adult with autism, writes convincingly of this strength and the need for families and professionals to capitalize on these visual strengths (Quill 1995). Many children with autism are also hyperlexic and can somehow break the fixed visual code with more ease than attending to the auditory message. This skill serves the population well as the team considers an augmentative means of communication.

Systems of Augmentative Communication in Autism

• PECS

• natural gestures

• signing

• vocalization/verbalization

• object systems

• picture systems

• written word

Picture Exchange Communication Systems (PECS) is a picture system devised by Frost and Bondy (1994). It has been used with great expectations with persons with autism. The concept of giving or exchanging a picture as a choice or request parallels true communication dyad interactions and engages a communicative partner.

Other systems of augmentative communication used by persons with autism include motoric systems, including the actual direct manipulation of another person to request an object or action. Natural gestures, pictures, written messages, and signing have all been used and paired with vocalization to augment the communication of persons with autism. As the child's reciprocal language skills increase, augmentative systems with voice output capabilities may be useful if verbal speech does not develop.

Janzen (1996) suggests that young children with autism are learning to communicate with more effectiveness due to a better understanding of the communication and processing deficits in autism as well as early diagnosis and intervention and the availability of augmentative systems.

Developmental Disabilities

Developmental disabilities can include a wide range of disorders and disabilities. We generally think of developmental disabilities as congenital in nature, although they may not be identified until children are toddlers or preschoolers. Developmental disabilities may be exhibited in all developmental domains, including motor, social, communicative, cognitive, and adaptive.

Developmental disabilities are often associated with chronic conditions resulting from lack of neurological development or from neurological impairment during the prenatal period (e.g., Down syndrome, neural tube deficits, exposure to toxic substances, maternal rubella). Perinatal causes can include prolonged labor, fetal distress, or anoxia during the birth process. Even following a healthy pregnancy and birth, developmental disabilities can occur. Causes during this time frame could include trauma, anoxia, toxins, and infectious processes. Sometimes the cause remains unknown.

Developmental Domains Affected

- motor
- social
- communicative
- cognitive
- adaptive

Persons with developmental disabilities present with many different individual profiles. Variances in cognitive abilities challenge the AAC team to determine linguistic level and appropriate goals for each individual. Suggestions for augmentative communication may range from very simple gestural systems to true symbolic use. Early communication skills of requesting, protesting, and making choices may be targeted initially. Later, more advanced linguistic skills may emerge, indicating the need for a more complex communication system. A team approach, that includes the family, is absolutely imperative.

Down Syndrome

Although most individuals with Down syndrome have some speech, their speech may be so unintelligible as to be ineffective for communicative purposes. A person with Down syndrome may also have significant language difficulties, or even a dual diagnosis, pairing the Down syndrome with another disorder often known to need AAC devices, such as severe hearing loss. A combination of communication modes using verbal, gesture, sign, and other forms of augmentative communication may be the best option for persons with Down syndrome.

Since infants and toddlers with Down syndrome are typically identified at birth or during gestation and are generally eligible for early intervention services from the time they are born, many are exposed to sign language from an early age. This form of augmentative communication can help to increase receptive as well as expressive language

Total Communication is a system that combines sign language and both receptive and expressive modes. Children with Down syndrome who use total communication can still develop speech, a very important factor to impress upon parents and caregivers. Signing may allow the young child the opportunity to affect his environment before he is able to verbally produce certain words. Kumin (1994) suggests that some first signs to teach include "more," "finished," and "no." These words carry strong functional intent and will assist the child in developing behavioral regulation skills.

The cognitive level and anatomical structure of the vocal tract of an individual with Down syndrome will influence the extent of intelligible verbal language development. As the child ages, he may continue to use gestures and sign language. Augmentative systems may not be the child's primary mode of communication, but can function as a supplementary or alternative system, particularly in contexts where sign is not understood or as a transitory system as the child develops speech. A full team evaluation is necessary to investigate the possibility of using such a system. Communication boards and books, gesture and signing systems, electronic devices, and Picture Exchange Communication System (PECS) have all been used in addition to verbalizations and vocalizations to optimize communication for persons with Down syndrome.

Dysarthria

Dysarthria refers to muscle weakness, incoordination, or paralysis in any part of the speech mechanism. There are various types of dysarthria and they can affect respiration, phonation, resonation, articulation, and prosody. Generally, speech which is labored, slow, and imprecise is called "dysarthric speech." Dysarthria is most often acquired and can be associated with causes such as cerebrovascular accident (CVA), traumatic brain injury (TBI), amyotrophic lateral sclerosis (ALS), and muscular dystrophy (MD).

Regardless of the diagnosis, augmentative communication should center around the provision of intelligible communication. Low-tech as well as high-tech recommendations from the team should be considered, and as these are often adult patients, functional living requirements must be considered.

Acquired Disorders

Having had the ability to speak and then losing this ability is a condition in which many people find themselves due to a variety of acquired disorders. This can include ALS (amyotrophic lateral sclerosis), multiple sclerosis, traumatic brain injury, cerebrovascular accident (stroke), Parkinson's disease, and others.

ALS is a disease which is progressive and degenerative with overall motor weakness. Approximate age of onset is 55, and there is a higher incidence of occurrence in men. The average life span for patients following onset is from three to five years. The majority of patients with ALS will be unable to speak by the time they die and thus will need alternative and augmentative communication services following the diagnosis.

Multiple sclerosis (MS) is a chronic disease which is often disabling. Patients may have the relapsing-remitting type, which means they will have periods of partial or total remission that can last from months to years. There are also progressive and secondary-progressive types of multiple sclerosis. Dyarthria is the most common communication problem associated with MS and would be the reason for AAC intervention.

Patients with traumatic brain injury may require differing approaches to AAC depending upon their phase of recovery. If the patient has recently recovered from a coma, a simple communication board may be appropriate. Middle and later stage recovery requires the matching of communication strategies to cognitive function.

Stroke patients can vary widely due to the diversity of etiology. Patients with Broca's aphasia, a nonfluent aphasia, will present differing needs than a patient with a brain stem lesion (Locked-In Syndrome).

Parkinson's disease presents a cluster of motor symptoms that include rigidity, a reduction in movement and tremor at rest. Articulation errors with inappropriate pauses and silences affect the output system of the patient. As the disease progresses, so will the need for AAC intervention.

Most often the clients seen by speech-language pathologists with these acquired disorders are adults. A hospital- or clinic-based service delivery model may be used. A team approach cannot be overemphasized as the medical professionals will be involved with these clients.

Assessment of Non-Speaking Communicators

3

Background

Practitioners have used various models of assessment in the past. Some early models focused on "candidacy;" that is, whether the individual possessed the necessary prerequisite skills for augmentative communication (Yorkston & Karlan 1986). Often these prerequisite skills included the ability to display cause and effect relationships and picture/symbol discrimination among others. When assessment candidates were physically older and had not yet developed these skills, they were typically determined "not ready" for a communication system. This "candidacy" model has been replaced by a model that seeks to teach those prerequisite skills associations if they are not yet developed in the individual with communication challenges.

A second approach is the Maximal Assessment Model (Glennen & DeCoste 1997), which focuses on extensive testing of all areas. This approach may include the use of standardized tests of receptive and expressive language, nonverbal speech and intelligence testing, measurements of communicative functions and modalities present, symbol/picture understanding and use, letter and/or word identification systems, and developmental checklists measuring specific communicative skills. Although this approach generally provides enough information to make a good decision for an augmentative system, it is difficult to achieve, given the time and resources required. This assessment model may be useful for beginning practitioners until they develop more competence and a greater comfort level in determining what information is needed to select appropriate equipment and plan effective interventions.

Experienced practitioners often rely on a predictive assessment or "feature-matching" assessment (Glennen & DeCoste 1997, King 1999). This type of assessment explores the individual's current communication status and determines the system of communication that best meets that individual's needs. This type of evaluation does not rely on standardized scores and numbers to select appropriate equipment, but rather matches the information from the individual with the equipment that is available and appropriate to move the current communication skills to the next level. The questions listed in the next section are formulated for use with a "feature-matched" assessment.

Assessment Questions

In any assessment, there are a number of questions to answer. Answering these questions provides a comprehensive picture of the individual and the communicative potential that the team is seeking.

What do we want to know?

Identifying the purpose for the assessment is paramount to achieving the results you desire in the end. Generally, the team attempts to determine what, if any, assistive devices or practices could help the non-speaking individual to communicate most effectively. The more specific the questions, the more likely you will be able to answer them during the assessment process.

There may be more than one question that the team wishes to answer. By specifically outlining the purpose for the evaluation, team members are more likely to focus on that aspect of the individual's communication and effectively target specific behaviors, opportunities, results, and equipment that will meet the purposes stated.

Assessment Team

- speech-language pathologist
- audiologist
- physical therapist
- occupational therapist
- psychologist
- social worker
- nurse
- educator(s)
- family/caregivers
- medical specialists
- rehabilitation engineer/assistive technologist

For example, the team may be looking for a way that the individual can answer questions in a classroom environment, order in a restaurant, or ride mass transit successfully. They may be looking for a more portable system than the device the individual currently uses for communication, or the team may be seeking a simple system for relaying information between school and home. Whatever the issue, the more clearly the question is outlined, the more assured you can be of gathering useful information.

Who do we need on the assessment team?

A team approach is essential in the assessment phase of servicing nonverbal communicators. Each assessment team member, including family members, brings a unique perspective to the assessment process.

Speech-Language Pathologist (SLP)

The knowledge of typical communication development, disordered communication development, and the ability to assess receptive and expressive language skills are trained skill areas for this professional. In addition, the SLP must be able to determine communicative intent and function from a nonverbal perspective. It is helpful if the SLP is familiar with a variety of communication systems and symbol choices (e.g., Rebus, traditional orthography). Often, but not always, the SLP leads the augmentative communication team.

Audiologist

The audiologist determines the hearing acuity of the individual. Significant findings may include auditory processing differences and any physical pathologies or abnormalities of the hearing channel that may interfere with communication. The audiologist may also assist in educational planning for the individual based on findings.

Physical Therapist

The physical therapist assists with the positioning of the individual for optimal communicative production. This professional's knowledge of positioning and range of motion for conserving effort on the part of communicators who are physically challenged may be helpful in maintaining communication for an extended period without over-taxing the individual's physical stamina. Adaptations and supports to seating and positioning aids may be recommended, as well as mobility aids to access educational opportunities.

Occupational Therapist (OT)

The OT is trained to determine fine motor skills and weaknesses that may affect the choice of an alternative communication system for a non-speaker. Pointing, grasping, splinting, and development of specifically designed tools are all within the domain of the OT. Many OTs are also trained in assistive technology, thereby enhancing their knowledge of communication systems for individuals who are unable to generate oral speech.

Psychologist

The team psychologist addresses present level of cognitive functioning and primary learning style. The psychologist may be a hospital-based professional, an individual in private practice, or a certified school psychologist. Both standardized and non-standardized assessment procedures (e.g., observations, developmental checklists, anecdotal notes) are used to determine present cognitive levels. Visual motor skill assessments may also be administered to obtain useful information.

Social Worker

The team social worker explores and documents family and medical history information, family structure, family priorities for the individual (e.g., being able to talk with grand-parent, join in prayers), cultural background, insurance status, and various family issues. This professional provides information to the family about the spectrum of programs and services available. In some settings, sources for funding an augmentative device may also be identified by the social worker.

Nurse

Gathering information concerning current health status, current medications, delivery of nursing care, physical limitations, and sharing information about the individual's disorder are part of the role of the nursing professional. It is also helpful for the nurse to provide information concerning prescripted medical intervention as needed.

Educator(s)

In the assessment process, the educator uses his knowledge of age-appropriate academic expectations to determine the strengths and weaknesses of the non-speaking student. Areas identified by this professional help plan remediation as well as identify positive teaching strategies, and build on the student's strengths in the intervention process. This professional can also provide information about socio-communicative opportunities in the classroom.

Family/Caregivers

Perhaps the team members with the most personal knowledge of the individual are the family members/caregivers involved in daily interactions with the individual. They are the experts in reading the person's signals, knowing his preferences and motivators, and having the opportunity for long term observation of the individual's abilities across a variety of contexts. From an outcome point of view, the family/caregiver has the most significant investment in the process for this individual.

Medical Specialists

The individual's physicians may offer a prognosis for improving or declining of skills based on the diagnosis. Those disorders with a static versus a dynamic course indicate differences in treatment and intervention approaches. A variety of medical professionals may be included on any particular team, and thorough understanding of their relevant medical reports is important for team planning.

Some of the medical specialists who may be involved in assessment teams for non-speaking individuals are the following.

- ophthalmologist

- otorhinolaryngologist (ENT)

- physiatrist (a medical doctor who specializes in rehabilitation)

- orthopedist

Rehabilitation Engineer/Assistive Technologist

A rehabilitation engineer or an assistive technologist may have a background in a field such as occupational therapy or engineering. This person's role on the team is to help identify the individual's ability to access the environment through use of technology and to be knowledgeable about technology available. This professional may also help design adaptive equipment for the individual.

Where should the evaluation take place?

During the assessment process, the ideal situation would be for the team to observe the individual in a variety of functional contexts.

For many teams, the luxury of seeing an individual in a variety of settings is not feasible. It then becomes the responsibility of the team to somehow gather information as to how the client communicates within those settings. A form to hand out to the individuals interacting with the potential augmentative user is helpful in collecting this information. A *Sample Communication Log* is included on page 40 and a blank form for your professional use on page 41.

Evaluation Settings

- home
- school or work
- riding to and from school/work activities (e.g., bus, car pool)
- community-based activities (e.g., restaurants, movies, grocery store)
- place of worship
- peer activities (e.g., Scouts, parties)
- family and caregiver interactions

Another decision the team must make is whether the entire team will see the individual at one time, or whether selected pairings of professionals will visit various environments at different times to assess the individual's skills. This team decision may vary on a case-by-case basis. At times, these decisions will be dictated by the availability of the staff selected for the team.

What do we already know about this individual?

Often the individuals referred for assessment have been receiving services from professionals for a period of time. Educators, therapists, and family members will already have a significant pool of information to use as a beginning point. This is important information because it provides a measure of skills developed and used over time as well as skills the user may possess but does not use on a regular basis because of difficulty or fatigue.

Assessment Issues

- communicative intent
- communicative functions
- pragmatic skills
- frequency and range of communicative attempts

Information about current communication levels may indicate the need for appropriate assessments or checklists to more accurately determine receptive and expressive language levels. Often formal testing of expressive and receptive language skills are not true representations of the individual's status due to motoric limitations. Therefore, the SLP or other team members must use developmental checklists and other references to determine the functional communicative status of the individual (e.g., *The Rossetti Infant-Toddler Language Scale, The Bzoch-League Receptive-Expressive Emergent Language Scale*).

Considerations must include communicative intent, communicative functions that may be present (or absent), pragmatic skills in communication, and the frequency and range of communicative attempts. These skills are all areas of focus in providing an augmentative system to supplement current communicative attempts.

The teacher, therapists, and family members/caregivers may indicate that the individual already understands routine events and shows anticipation, indicating the presence of some memory capabilities. They may indicate certain tasks or textures that the individual enjoys or dislikes. These items then can be part of the assessment to determine the user's ability to accurately select items that are desirable and to avoid any undesirable items.

Teachers, therapists, and family members/caregivers can also give information as to what kind of input the individual already understands (e.g., symbols [getting his shoes means "we're going outside"], pictures, written words). Knowing what input the individual understands may assist the team in determining the symbol representation system to use as a starting place for an augmented communication system.

There may be positioning and fine motor issues that are already known, and strategies that have been attempted, either successfully or unsuccessfully. Knowledge of this background should save the team time in assessing what works best for this individual. Additional assessment for specific switches, pointing, or other adaptations may be initiated if more information is needed in this area.

Identifying special communication partners or activities the individual enjoys will allow the team to observe these interactions and use them as a starting point for augmented communication. From the elements observed in the interaction, the team can develop strategies to scaffold on the current exchange to expand communications. For example, if a child always smiles and slaps his lap tray when a special friend enters the room, you could place a switch on the lap tray with a greeting for that person, or a general message for room visitors. The message might even include a question (e.g., "Hi Gretchen! What did you do last night?") that invites the receiver to interact with the augmented user. By replacing the nonverbal activity with the switch-activated voice output, you have enriched the communicative exchange by at least one turn.

Understanding the communication needs of the individual is another important issue in addressing augmentative communication. What is it that the individual needs to communicate, or is motivated enough to ask for, that will not happen during the normal course of the day if he waits? Often those involved with selection and implementation of the augmentative communication device will ask that "bathroom, nap, food," and/or "drink" be included on an initial communication system, but usually the individual gets these primary needs satisfied without having to ask.

For some individuals with severe physical and cognitive challenges, it may be difficult to determine a reinforcer strong or desirable enough to elicit an initial communicative exchange. It may be helpful to use a systematic approach to sensory system stimulation to determine desirable and undesirable items for these individuals (Korsten et al. 1989). This system is described in more detail on page 53.

Communication Logs

Often nonverbal individuals communicate through gestures or behaviors that are understood by those most familiar with them. If this information is documented on a "communication log," it can be invaluable to the team in understanding the types of messages the individual presently communicates. A communication log records and describes the following information.

- the behavior that the individual does
  (e.g., "Johnny blinks his eyes several times in a row.")

- what that behavior means (e.g., "He wants a drink.")

- what the response of the caregiver is
  (e.g., "I hold up the water and the juice and he looks at the one he wants.")

Reviewing this type of behavior list can be invaluable to the assessment team, but is also a valuable tool to pass along to teachers, therapists, and respite care or baby-sitting providers. (See the *Sample Communication Log* on page 40 and a blank log on page 41.) This list of behaviors can often provide clues as to what elements of the environment the individual currently tries to control and where augmented communication may be most successfully introduced.

Sample Communication Log

Student/Client _____ Date _____ Page _____

Behavior (What does the individual do?)	Communication (What do you think it means?)	Response (What do you do when it happens?)	Frequency (How often does this happen?)	Date Noted/ Comments
Johnny blinks his eyes several times in a row.	He wants a drink.	I hold up two choices and he looks at the one he wants.	Occurs about 4 times during lunch and about twice during other times of the day	12-10-02: He's been doing this for about a week now.

Communication Log

Student/Client _____   Date _____   Page _____

Behavior (What does the individual do?)	Communication (What do you think it means?)	Response (What do you do when it happens?)	Frequency (How often does this happen?)	Date Noted/ Comments

Ecological Inventory

In addition to documenting how an individual currently communicates, it is also helpful to complete an ecological inventory of the individual's communication environments to determine situations in which he is expected to communicate but has no available means to do so. See the *Sample Ecological Inventory* on page 43 and the blank form for your professional use on page 44. This ecological survey can be one complete day, several 20-minute time blocks throughout the day, or some other time arrangement. A teacher, aide, parent, therapist, or any other member of the team familiar with the individual can complete it. Opportunities for interaction that are missed because the individual has no way to respond with the current communication system should be documented. This documentation often serves as a beginning point for planning intervention.

·42·

Sample Ecological Inventory

Student/Client _____ Date _____

Observer _____

Location of Observation _____ Time of Day _____

Length of Observation _____ Activity Observed _____

Missed or Incorrect Use Opportunity	How communicated (if attempted)	What others (peers) communicated
weather portion of calendar time	pointed at the window	"sunny," "cold," etc.
math equation activity	raised hand, but did not communicate when called on	"more" or "less"

Ecological Inventory

Student/Client _____   Date _____

Observer _____

Location of Observation _____   Time of Day _____

Length of Observation _____   Activity Observed _____

Missed or Incorrect Use Opportunity	How communicated (if attempted)	What others (peers) communicated

Individual Preferences

There may be information about the individual's preferences (e.g., auditory, textural, visual) that will contribute to the decision making process.

- Auditory—You may want to demonstrate both digitized and synthesized speech output for the individual and look for a preference or aversion to one or the other.

- Textural—There may be issues of textures the person prefers or avoids that would aid in selecting one system over another.

- Visual—Some individuals may prefer or require line drawings as opposed to photographs, or vice versa. Size of the stimulus required is another important factor to explore with the individual.

The speed with which a user can scan an overlay of pictures and select the appropriate choice may lead to selecting a dynamic screen arrangement or a static display device. The ability to generate more abstract ideas and relationships between words and pictures may indicate the ability to use a system with semantic compaction (e.g., to communicate "red" in Minspeak, the user would access a picture of a rainbow for "colors," then a picture of an apple for "red") as opposed to a more explicit, single meaning arrangement. Even consideration of whether the user is a "fashion trend setter" or oblivious to this aspect can be important information to gather. This exploration will help you match the features of the desired communication system to the abilities and preferences of the user and will increase the probability that the system will be accepted and used.

How do we determine needed features in a communication device?

An assessment kit can be a useful tool in considering a variety of factors as you match the features a communicator needs to a communication system. The contents of an individual kit may vary by population assessed, but there are some basics that allow a variety of tasks to be accomplished that can help to determine the most beneficial features for the user.

If you are working with an individual who has a variety of interests already identified (e.g., music, reading, sports), consider using that information to select items that will be motivating. Levels of sophistication vary widely given the cognitive abilities, motoric abilities, and communicative interest of the candidate for augmented communication.

What is the next communicative step for this individual?

As you examine the individual's current communication status, the question becomes "What is the next step that augmented communication can provide?" If the person presently communicates by pointing at pictures, this may be a time to explore whether voice output attached to that picture (through use of a simple device) would increase the individual's communicative status. If the person currently uses a picture exchange system, it may be worth exploring the complexity of that system to determine the level of syntactic complexity that is being used and whether the system can be expanded.

Establishing Baselines

It is helpful to collect baseline data on the individual's communication status prior to or during the assessment process to document whether changes provided with augmented systems are truly moving communication skills forward. Such documentation may include the number of interactions in a given time period, the complexity of those interactions, the number of functions accomplished by the current communications system, and the ability to continue an interaction with the current system.

Given this baseline and using the ecological survey information described on page 42, decisions can be made as to appropriate expansions or extensions of current communication skills to meet the next communicative step of the individual. Consideration must be given to whether the person will benefit from a single-word or phrase-based communication system. Often those in the individual's environment will desire a phrase-based system for social appropriateness. However, it is important to remember that if you wish to promote language development to eventually lead to reading and writing skills, a single-word system with the ability to generate two- and three-word combinations may be a more appropriate first step.

What features are needed for the communication system this individual would use to address the identified needs?

Communication Systems Features

• non-vocal system
  (e.g., sign, picture exchange)

• digitized or synthesized speech

• static or dynamic display

• access mode (direct or indirect)

• scanning speed requirements (if needed)

• portability and/or mountability of the device

• ease of programming

Given all the information you have collected up to this point in the assessment, the decision about the appropriate piece(s) of technology for this individual should be an effort to match the identified needs with features of a particular device or devices. There may be different pieces of technology to accomplish different functions throughout the individual's activities, thus the idea of a system would be more appropriate than restricting the individual to only one communication mode for all situations. This information will help you select appropriate equipment for the evaluation in the hands-on segment described below.

One strategy is to identify the features a system must provide. As you begin to answer questions, you will identify which parameters best suit the purposes for the user. Then you can select the most appropriate types of devices, based on examination of their features listed in Chapter 1.

How are the findings of this assessment documented?

Generally when the evaluation is complete, some type of documentation or report is needed. The format and complexity of this report may depend on the target audience. How the report is shared and who it is shared with will depend on how you intend to use the report and what role others will play in the implementation of the communication system. Knowing possible funding sources and report requirements will ensure that necessary data is gathered during the hands-on evaluation. More information on writing reports, documenting findings, procuring funding, and teaming for success can be found in Chapter 6.

Hands-On Evaluation

Working with an individual during an augmentative communication evaluation is a combination of art and science. Initially, many AAC evaluation teams are more comfortable with the science portions (e.g., obtaining measurements and "hard" data), but eventually, with experience, the team becomes more intuitive and efficient in matching the AAC user and his environment to specific equipment and intervention strategies.

One factor to consider is that, depending on the nature of the individual's disability and associated fatigue and/or inattention factors, you may have a limited amount of time with the client for the evaluation. It is best to schedule at least two visits and to allow for opportunities to gather information from the individual's caregivers as well as to observe the individual in a typical environment.

A period of observation of the individual in the environment you are targeting (at least initially) is generally helpful. For teams evaluating school-age clients, this may be the child's classroom. For adults, this may be the individual's residence or workplace. Observations may indicate that the individual demonstrates some basic cognitive skills (e.g., cause/effect, object permanence, means/end) that can be documented without specific testing. If these skills are present, there is no need to evaluate them in the hands-on session. The observation may also reveal communicative functions (e.g., requesting, commenting, greetings, protests) that the individual uses through alternative means. These functions can be used to explore other communication modalities that could meet and expand the communicator's needs, including those that are nonverbal but functional. During the observation, also note any favorite items, activities, or materials that interest the client.

If the client has motoric challenges, the observation can serve as a time to identify movements the individual can make independently and consistently. Watch for and note movements the client appears to have control over. These movements may suggest switch access sites if the individual is unable to access a device by direct selection. Note whether the individual is able to point or hold a pencil or other instrument and release it without difficulty. All of these movements will become more important when the client attempts to use a communication system.

Generally, for the initial evaluation, it may be helpful to remove the individual from a group situation to a more controlled, less stimulating environment where he can focus on the tasks presented. If the client has a caregiver who knows him well, it may be beneficial to have the caregiver in the room to answer questions or interpret the individual's responses.

Consider each of the areas addressed by the feature-match system explained on page 46. Not all will need to be directly evaluated. By establishing certain parameters (e.g., the individual can access by direct selection), you will be able to move forward without assessing related skills (e.g., the individual's ability to use switches). The goal of using the assessment kit and objects and activities that the individual finds motivating is to determine whether (and how) this person can access communication technology and use it with purpose as an adjunct to his current communication system.

Augmentative communication evaluations begin in various places and take on different characteristics depending on the cognitive and communicative level of the client. As you look at the general functioning level of the client, you will narrow your focus to features that are truly functional for that client.

Hands-On Evaluation

- switch users vs. direct selection

- beginning communicators—no known reinforcers

- beginning communicators—known reinforcers

- communicators—no effective system

- communicators with system—needing more advanced system

- areas of assessment

    communication environments
    matching tools and technology
    communication devices in the hands of a first time user

Direct Selection Vs. Switch Users

Identifying the appropriate access mode for an individual is critical to the implementation of any effective system. Depending on the system selected, the motor requirements may differ. These factors must be included when selecting a system.

If the individual is able, direct selection with one or both hands is typically the most desirable access method with an electronic device. Direct selection typically allows the quickest responses and initiation of communication. To assess whether direct selection is available, the occupational therapist may help explore the following:

- hand strength

- client's ability to use a finger point or a tool to activate a device

- range of motion and reach (part of determining the size of the device)

- size of the target the client can accurately activate (determines the size of the individual locations)

- whether a keyguard could assist in accurate selection (to avoid activations created by inadvertent movements, such as dragging the hand or pointing with two fingers simultaneously)

Evaluation activities to address these skills may include the following:

- attempts to activate actual devices presented to the individual

- watching the individual use a computer keyboard or electronic toy with buttons

- using evaluation boards with different sized "targets" and different sized areas marked off to determine range and accuracy

- using a computer with a touch screen and software requiring various degrees of accuracy on targets

- observing the person attempt to pick up small objects (e.g., raisins)

Direct Selection

If the individual can use his hands for direct selection, this is the fastest and generally the most desirable method. The next best alternative would be some type of implement in the hand, or a head stick or mouth stick to activate the device. This selection method still has the speed of the direct-select method, even if the hands are not available as direct selection options.

If the individual has the use of his hands but has difficulty accurately targeting a specific location (e.g., drags his hand across a number of locations enroute to the desired item), this limitation can result in miscommunications. In this case, explore using a keyguard to determine if it allows more effective access to the device. Different devices have different keyguard designs, some with more open spaces and some with smaller openings. Some are clear and others are opaque. Depending on the type of movement, accuracy difficulties, and visual perceptual issues the individual exhibits, different keyguard types may be selected or fabricated.

One more type of direct select available on some but not all devices is infrared technology. Using a light beam attached to the eyeglasses, the brim of a baseball cap, or even a headband may be an appropriate activation method. To use such a system, the communicator must be able to scan the pictures and match the beam from his headgear to the receiver on the device. Once this connection is made, a "dwell time" on that receiver activates the icon to produce the message. Dwell time indicates how long the beam must be lined up with the receiving beam before the device activates the selection. Dwell times can typically be adjusted to match the speed and dexterity of the communicator with the infrared pointer. If the dwell time is too short, there may be accidental activations of the device.

An emerging technology takes the infrared technology a step further and combines the infrared technology on the device with an adhesive reflecting dot placed on the user's forehead. Reflected light from the device activates the beam and makes the selection. This technology would be appropriate for individuals who demonstrate strong, independent head control and use without excessive fatigue. Like the infrared pointer, dwell time can be adjusted.

Switch Users

If direct selection does not appear to be an option for the user, a switch may be appropriate. Switches come in a multitude of shapes and sizes and can be configured for almost any voluntary movement an individual possesses.

Switch Activation Modes

- depress and release
- "sweep" movement
- breath control
- head grip and release
- minimal muscle movement
- voice
- hand moisture

Many switches involve using a body movement to depress and release a contact. These switches come in a variety of shapes and sizes. One selection factor is to consider the smallest switch that the user can accurately and efficiently use. Aesthetic elements of augmentative communi-cation often become a reason that devices and systems are abandoned, so consideration needs to be given to making the switch size, sound, and location as unobtrusive as possible while still maintaining easy access to the device it is activating. An important consideration for individuals who fatigue easily is the degree of effort or intensity needed to activate various switches.

In addition to switches that are activated by depressing and releasing, there are switches that can be activated by a "sweep" movement. That is, the user moves his arm, hand, or leg across the activation target and does not need the ability to depress and release the switch.

Other switches are activated by breath control (e.g., sip and puff switches), hand grip and release, minimal muscle movements (e.g., clenching a jaw, blinking the eyes, or moving an eyebrow), voice activation (e.g., any type of vocalization), or even activated by the moisture in the touch of the hand. Switch technology continues to develop, so the use of up-to-date resources (e.g., Web sites and feature-matching) to select possible switches for the user will continue to develop as well. In summary, one of the initial considerations for selecting a switch is identifying what movements are reliable, controllable, and independent for the user to activate a switch.

Part of this determination can be accomplished in the observation period. After watching the individual's movements in unstructured and structured situations, you may be able to determine if there are voluntary movements the individual could use to access a switch. On the other hand, the evaluation team also needs to consider any involuntary movements the user may demonstrate that would cause inadvertent activations.

Following the observation, the only way to ensure that a user can activate a switch consistently and reliably is to try it. The problem, of course, is that not each evaluation team has access to all of the equipment all of the time. If the equipment you have is not adequate and you feel there is another switch that could work for the user, you can typically purchase a switch to try from a manufacturer for a period of 30 or 60 days, and then return the switch if it does not work. This process is cumbersome in terms of time and effort, but it allows you to find an appropriate switch without spending money on a switch the user cannot access well. If you have selected the most appropriate switch type and placement, you have taken a major step forward in ensuring the use of the augmentative system by the user for the future.

During the evaluation, you must also determine what the switch will activate. Often where you begin to explore will depend on your perception of the user's abilities to understand that he can cause changes in his environment. If you are not sure that the cause/effect relationship is present, you may wish to begin with a simple switch toy or an environmental control unit with a string of lights, a fan, or other favorite activity of the user. You will look for whether the individual can access the switch as well as whether he understands that he is controlling the environment using the switch. For example, if you have connected the switch to a toy with a designated "routine" (e.g., a bear that sings a song or a dog that jumps a back flip), does the individual wait for the routine to end before activating the switch again? If not, you may begin to question whether the individual understands he is causing the action by activating the switch. If you are not sure this skill and understanding is present, look for ideas to teach cause/effect in Chapter 5. If the user appears to have the idea, then the purpose of the activity becomes to find the most appropriate switch fit.

Another skill necessary for switch users of augmented communication devices is the ability to scan an array of pictures/words and time the switch activation to select the desired item.

Elements of Scanning

• timing of the scan

• sequence or order of the scan

• whether the scan always begins at the same point or resumes at the point of previous activation

• whether the user requires an auditory cue to scan due to attention or vision impairments

---

Scanning often involves a higher cognitive load of memory, timing of motor movements, and more attentional abilities than direct access. Some of these skills can be improved with use of the device or supplemented with scanning software for computers that use a switch interface. Examples of these programs are listed in the software references in Appendixes B and C, pages 130-132.

Beginning Communicators—No Known Reinforcers

One of the first questions for individuals who lack functional communication is "What does this person want that he cannot get on his own?" Requesting is one of the earliest language functions to develop and remains an important communication component throughout a lifetime. It is imperative to find things the person enjoys in order to begin to teach him to ask for what he wants. It should be noted that some individuals typically are not using another method to communicate (e.g., pointing, gesturing), but rather are passive observers waiting for things to happen to them throughout their day. Sometimes parents and caregivers cannot even identify pleasurable events or rewards these individuals enjoy.

One method of determining desired reinforcers is to present a variety of stimuli and then check for reactions. Especially in individuals with severe disabilities, this process can involve monitoring pulse rate, breathing rate, facial expressions, and body postures when various stimuli are presented. One tool that helps organize and document these initial reactions and ensures that all sensory modalities are explored is the *Every Move Counts* program (Korsten et al. 1993). (See Appendix D, pages 133-139.)

Using this systematic and data-based recording system, the assessment team introduces a given stimuli three times to determine the individual's reaction. The timing and recording of the input requires a team of at least two, but this assessment moves fairly quickly once the evaluators are familiar with the process. What the evaluation team looks for is any response from the individual (positive, negative, or no response) based on body posture or tone, facial expressions, vocalizations, or other indications of pleasure or discomfort. The items determined as desirable are then used as reinforcers to begin a basic symbol-association communication system.

The *Every Move Counts* program provides data sheets and examples of sensory inputs for tactile, auditory, visual, olfactory, gustatory, and vestibular stimuli. A training videotape is also available. A protocol is recommended for presenting each stimulus and judging the reaction, based on the individual's overall body reactions. The beginning steps for initiating communication requests based on information gathered are provided in the manual.

Beginning Communicators—Known Reinforcers

For individuals who already have desired reinforcers, an evaluation can determine what symbols to use to extend their present communication system. Identifying a symbol system that can represent their desired items is an important part of the evaluation.

Using known reinforcers, symbols, and pictures can determine if the individual can understand the connection between the representation and the object/action he desires. As part of the assessment, you may use miniatures of the item or pictures.

Appropriate Pictures

- conventional photographs

- digital photographs

- labels from packages or magazines depicting the reinforcer

- line drawings in black-and-white or color

Initially, allow several trials for the user to select the reinforcer(s) to ensure that he understands the connection between requesting and receiving the reinforcer. If the user successfully demonstrates these skills, then you may wish to work on discrimination skills to determine that he will scan an array and then select desired items. The only way to assess whether the individual is truly selecting things he desires is to add undesirable choices. For example, if you have a child who will work for computer time, put that selection on his board as well as a choice for something he does not like (e.g., reading time). If he makes the undesired choice, you give him the natural consequence.

·53·

Features to examine during this evaluation phase include overlay features (e.g., color, size, type, number, layout) and the ability to combine pictures to create phrases or sentences. Also consider the anticipated ability of the individual to combine selections to create utterances for new situations. The ability to generate novel utterances by combining available choices would parallel a natural stage in language acquisition. If a client consistently signals "eat," then allowing for many choices to pair with "eat" would create innumerable possibilities.

Intervention targets might include consideration of typical language development for young children and situational needs for individuals of all ages (Goossens, Crain, and Elder 1992). For example, if a client is communicating by two-word combinations and seems ready to more on to three-word combinations, those choices to assist in this transition must be available. (More information on this scripting approach is discussed in Chapter 5.)

Communicators—No Effective System

Some individuals appear to convey a great deal of information without a dedicated augmentative system. However, some of these individuals have developed a series of "looks," body postures, gestures, or signals to communicate basic wants, needs, and responses that are understood only by those who are closest to them. For this group of individuals, the goal of the assessment and intervention is typically either to expand their available repertoire or to find a system that will allow them to convey their established messages with a system that is understood by a wider group of communication partners. These goals are not mutually exclusive, but knowing the outcome expected of the evaluation is important to ensure that the goal is reached through effective assessment and intervention.

If the individual has limited motoric abilities, much of the same assessment described in the previous section for access to a device or switch (pages 47-51) should be conducted. Once the access mode is identified, the next step is to address current communications; identify functions the individual already demonstrates; and determine what, if any, additional communications are needed.

An excellent resource to use for this type of data gathering is information from the individual's primary caregivers as described in a communication log. A sample form can be found on page 40. The communication log should contain the following information:

• signal the communicator uses

• perceived intent of the communication

• typical response by the caregiver

Communication Log Excerpts

• "When Susie raises her eyebrows and looks toward the windows, she is telling me she's hot. So then I either remove excess clothing, turn on the fan, or open the window for her."

• "When my child has a headache, he will take any toy around and start to push it into his forehead. When he does this, I give him 2 teaspoons of acetaminophen."

A blank *Communication Log* for recording this data is found on page 41. Using this information, you can begin to determine the complexity of the communication the individual has already established. You can also use this information to help determine the appropriate number of choices on a communication board or device the individual could use for communication. You cannot assume that the individual will immediately use the new system because he already has a system that works to communicate many needs and wants. What the system will do for this user is to allow him to expand his requests and communicate with new people who do not understand his unique requesting and communicating behaviors.

Again, depending on the physical abilities of the individual (e.g., vision, access, cognition), you should determine what type of symbol system might work best. Any limitations of range, size, or type of icons will impact the type of system recommended. Another consideration for this user is the complexity of the current system. The more complex the current signaling system is, the more likely it is that the individual will be able to learn and use a more complex system to convey novel phrases and utterances. An individual with less cognitive ability and a less elaborate signaling system may benefit from a simpler communication system that reduces the cognitive load to generate utterances.

Communicators with System—Needing a More Advanced System

Sometimes an individual who has been using a system of one type will indicate that the system is no longer adequate to meet his needs. Recognizing this fact can be difficult because each person who is limited in his communicative output may not react similarly. For some, the response is to generate fewer communications per day. Since they are unable to communicate their desired message, they simply say nothing in those situations. Others will attempt to join existing words or phrases in unique ways to convey new meanings. Yet others will demonstrate increased signaling or frustration with their limitations. Whatever the manifestation, the message that should be clear is that the current communication system is not meeting the individual's needs.

Areas of Assessment

- receptive language
- current expressive language system
- reading and spelling level
- written output

Receptive language skills can be measured by responses to questions, anticipation of events described, and sense of humor. Some standardized measures may be available (e.g., *Receptive One-Word Picture Vocabulary Test* [ROWPVT], *Peabody Picture Vocabulary Test* [PPVT-III], *Test for Auditory Comprehension of Language* [TACL-3], receptive portions of *The Preschool Language Scale-3* [PLS-3]), depending on the abilities of the communicator to respond with points or signals.

After assessing receptive language abilities, try to advance the expressive language system to levels that closely align with measured receptive abilities. Combining two words or phrases may be the next level, or it may involve moving from picture-based systems to word-based systems to allow for longer, more specific utterances. Examining the current system and the communicator's needs and opportunities not currently being met should help determine how the vocabulary system for the user should change.

The reading and spelling level of the individual should also be assessed. Again, standardized testing may be available if the individual is able. If not, informal measures of matching letters to sounds (and vice versa), the ability to recognize basic sight words, and the ability to match words to pictures may yield valuable information that includes or rules out the use of a spelling-based system. The advantage of word prediction systems is that they assist in speed of production and sometimes in reducing spelling difficulties as well. More information on word prediction systems is available in Chapter 5.

Just as language is the basis for reading, speaking is an important component in generating written content. Therefore, a more syntactically correct system of communication may be the next developmental step for the individual who is communicating with limited phrases and pictures. More complex systems will allow the individual to directly print out messages generated by the augmentative communication system. These messages can then be used as computer documents—edited and revised as needed for the circumstance. Further discussion of the interrelationship between augmentative communication and literacy is discussed in Chapter 5.

Communication Environments

Often individuals are seen in only one context or on one day for a complete assessment of their communicative needs. Numerous environmental factors may interfere with or facilitate natural or augmented communication. One of the essential reasons for an assessment by a team, rather than one individual, is to ensure that each professional addresses communication from the point of view with which they are most familiar. Assessment should include the regular parts of a day for the individual (e.g., school or work, home, transitions on the bus or in a car, meal times, recess, or breaks). The augmentative communication evaluation should also include things that do not occur on a regular basis, but do involve communicative needs and opportunities (e.g., going to a restaurant, going to the doctor, making a purchase in a store, using the telephone).

If an individual is dependent on others for mobility and seating/positioning issues, it is important to address whether he can access the device while in his chair, as well as other daily positions in which he is expected or anticipated to communicate. For example, the switch placement that works in his wheelchair may not be appropriate for his use in the stander or in a side-lying position. Perhaps the individual spends his school days primarily in his wheelchair, but his home time is spent on a couch or in a hospital bed. The assessment team needs to address these adaptations for alternate access with the family if the system selected is to be implemented across environments.

Matching Tools and Technology

As the team considers the needs of the individual and the various environments, assessment inevitably crosses over into intervention. Identifying whether the primary system selected is functional for some, most, or all of the user's environments will lead the team to determine secondary systems or additional needs of the primary system for the user. Without the input of all members, environments that are important for the user may be overlooked. Use of a model that matches the individual, environment, task, and technology is essential for finding an appropriate array of communication components for an individual (Zabala 2002).

Communication Devices in the Hands of a First-Time User

Part of the assessment activity is to systematically present options to the individual to understand the level of language competence he has and to attempt the feature-match activities that were discussed on pages 46-52. Often when given a device or pictures for the first time, the individual will immediately begin to push all of the buttons or touch pictures without waiting for a response from the communicative partner. If you have given thoughtful consideration to your assessment kit and the individual's preferences, you will have selected pictures/word/icon symbols that represent desired items.

If the individual does not appear to understand the power of the communication device to impact the environment, you may wish to limit the number of choices and reinforcers to those that are highly tangible and somewhat concrete. For example, you may want to look at access on a 32-location device with 1-inch square locations. If the individual is initially overwhelmed with all 32 choices, program only three or four squares on the device and use highly desired reinforcers. If the user is pushing buttons randomly, you may need to assist him in selecting one of the programmed squares, and remove the device as you present the reinforcer. This sequence may need to happen several times before the user begins to understand the pairing between requesting with the device and obtaining the desired reinforcer. You will know the pairing has taken place when the individual activates a message and waits or looks expectantly for the reinforcer.

Depending on the individual's nonverbal abilities, you may want to explore a more complex system than single messages. Choosing among a variety of pre-programmed software requires that you assess certain linguistic skills. For example, it may be important to understand categorization skills if you are planning to use the Unity software from Prentke-Romich. In this software, all foods begin with the "apple" symbol. If it is Mexican food, the second activation is the "cactus." The final activation determines the specific food item based either on beginning letter of the word (also on the overlay) or the likeness of the picture to the food item depicted. This system may require more cognitive load than other systems using a dynamic screen to change the options on each page.

Current reading and spelling abilities and the potential for further development should be explored during the evaluation. Some users will benefit from word prediction capabilities on a device to access novel words for communication. These abilities can be explored using a computer with word prediction software or with an augmentative communication device with word prediction capabilities. On these programs, you are generally able to arrange the keyboard layout in either the standard keyboard layout (QWERTY) or in alphabetical order with each row beginning with a vowel.

Some communicators will immediately understand the purpose and power of a communication system. For others, these skills will need to be targeted and taught. These communicative needs are then matched with the environmental assessment for the communicator and priorities are established.

Regardless of the level of understanding, some consideration must be given as to whether auditory output of a system is beneficial or necessary for the communicator or the audience. For some communicators the auditory message is a distraction, for others a necessity. The reaction of the client to the message should be considered as a variable in the feature match for selecting a device. For example, if a client has distractibility issues, a voice output may confuse him.

If the individual initially understands the function and purpose of the communication device, the complexity of language and the most appropriate symbol system to use becomes the next consideration. There is currently great debate and research targeted at determining the most appropriate system to allow augmented communicators to generate novel messages while at the same time maintaining a speed of conversation adequate to sustain the interaction (Higginbotham 2001).

The assessment forms on pages 140-150 describe skills to be evaluated, components to explore, and possible assessment strategies and target outcome measures. This matrix provides a guide for the team as it moves through the assessment process and identifies needed components of an augmentative communication system for the individual.

Sharing the Assessment and Coming to Consensus

It is important to remember that as important as a good evaluation and an appropriate choice of equipment may be for an individual, the greatest emphasis must be placed on what happens afterward. Simply providing equipment does not make someone a communicator any more than providing a wrench makes you a car mechanic. It is the knowledge of how to use the tool effectively that is needed to be successful, as well as the support and encouragement to implement an AAC system.

To be successful at the point of implementation, the team must start building consensus early in the process. Some consensus will occur during the gathering of information and "hands-on" portions of the evaluation, but at that point, the work is just beginning. While determining funding sources, finalizing the report, and exploring possible device suppliers, keeping members informed and "on the same page" can lead to a more unified approach and optimal use of the system later.

Evaluation Report

In some format following the evaluation, you must share findings and build a consensus about the communication system to be implemented for the individual. Often, a written report is required to document the findings of the team. It is important to know the audience expected to use this report. Sometimes there is more than one audience, and this situation may require more than one evaluation report.

Reports written by teams in school-based settings often address classroom expectations, current levels of performance, and curricular issues as well as areas in which the student struggles to participate, due to communication limitations. In reports written by hospital-based teams, the focus is more often on the medical needs and the performance of the individual on one particular day. The school-based team often has the benefit of watching a student grow, mature, and communicate over a period of time, as well as across people, environments, and tasks. Given the nature of the medical model, evaluations at hospitals are often conducted in the hospital or clinic without the benefit of seeing the individual participate in multiple settings.

Purpose of the Report

Regardless of who writes the evaluation report, it is paramount to consider the purpose of the report. If the report is designed only to assist in implementing or expanding the current system, the emphasis may well be on specific strategies and situations in which the device could be better used. If the report is being written for acquisition of an augmentative communication system, the required components and guidelines of the funding source often drive the format of the report.

Essential Components of an Effective Report

Regardless of the reporting requirements, the report should include documentation of all findings from the assessment conducted. These would include the following:

- the communicator's demographic data (e.g., date of birth, age, present living arrangements)

- names and titles of those on the evaluation team, and the date(s) the evaluation was conducted

- relevant medical and social background information (e.g., surgeries completed or anticipated, medications, periods of regression, ongoing seizures)

- etiology of the speech difficulty including date (if appropriate) and interventions attempted since that time to develop (or regain) oral speech production

- present levels of communicative functioning

- measures of language and cognitive development

- documentation of communication needs observed/reported and methods currently used to address those needs

- motor abilities and limitations

- vision and hearing status

- results of "hands on" observation and evaluation conducted by the team

- documentation of any trial periods conducted as part of the evaluation

Writing for Families and School Staff

The report must be user-friendly to the intended target audience. Therefore, if parents, spouses, or other non-medical professionals are expected to read the report, it is important to select language that will provide a comfortable reading level with familiar terms the audience can understand. The information should reflect how the evaluation team decided on which feature match elements were necessary, which elements could be beneficial in the future, and which elements would not be needed for this particular communicator. By providing (and agreeing) on the rationale for the features of the system, everyone is essentially agreeing on what the communication system will be and what is expected in terms of using the system.

Sometimes photographs or drawings of specific positioning ideas for switches and equipment may be helpful as additions to the written specifications. For some individuals, videotaped excerpts may be helpful in this transition phase as well as the implementation phase to document current user abilities via a method other than written words.

If the team has identified any particular implementation strategies that appeared promising during the evaluation or trial periods, they should also be documented in the report. Then all providers who may benefit from that information will have access to it, whether or not they are able to attend meetings, staffings, and evaluation sessions.

Writing for Outside Agencies

If the report is for an insurance company, Medicaid, Medicare, or private charity organization to provide funding for a more complex device, there may need to be more technical language, measurements, and specificity of terms to improve chances of securing funding. Many times the report format may be dictated by the insurer, and although it may seem redundant or obtuse to the evaluation, it is important to complete the evaluation report in the outlined format to increase chances of a positive outcome on the first submission to a funding source. Specific examples of the technical language necessary for successful report writing can be found in the funding section of this chapter (pages 67-70), as well as some sample case studies for individuals with a variety of disabilities (pages 93-94, 100-101, 106-107, and 114-115).

Finalizing the Report

When the augmentative communication evaluation report is drafted, a team meeting can be held to discuss findings, share insights, and discuss possible options prior to finalizing the report. This meeting should include both the evaluation team and the implementation team if the team participants differ. Caretakers can share their information and vision for the type(s) of systems selected for the individual. Whenever feasible, the augmentative communication user should also be part of this discussion so that person's reactions and concerns to the systems discussed can be considered. Communicative priorities should be discussed by those who know the individual well and those familiar with situations where the communicator currently lacks the ability to make her message known.

In addition to identifying initial targets for communication, some discussion of needed maintenance, programming, and repairs for the equipment selected should also be addressed. Who will be responsible for such tasks, what training and/or resources are available, and what support will be needed should be determined and included in the evaluation report. The evaluation report should also include a plan for implementing the device across various settings.

Awareness of Cultural/Personal Differences

- at home

- at school

- in the community

It is widely accepted that social language requirements and expectations change with the environment and audience to be addressed. Most agree that speaking at home on topics that are often routine allows us to speak in less formal structures and vocabulary than a meeting with the director of the hospital or the superintendent of a school system. Therefore, it follows that different "cultures"—whether work, home, school, or community—may have different language expectations, needs, and requirements. Do not mistake this as one "language" being superior to another, but rather recognize that the system must be flexible enough to meet the needs of the user across environments.

Some families do not want their child to use an AAC system because they fear it will inhibit speech development or cause their child to appear "different" in public. Another consideration often difficult for school personnel to accept is that communication systems are often used at school and on community outings through the school, but little care or implementation occurs in the home. Teams must respect that caregivers at home often know the individual so well and routines at home are so well established for the benefit of everyone that eye gaze, head turns, and other ritualized movements have developed into an intimate communication system that is comfortable for both parties. This may be the most efficient way for them to communicate and should be respected, although the individual may need alternatives in situations where that particular caregiver is not present.

Sensitivity to cultural differences is often overlooked in considering augmentative communication. Hourcade, Parette, and Huer (2002) discuss family involvement in all types of assistive technological use and how the failure to involve families in these decisions can lead to device abandonment. The consideration of any technological device, especially augmentative communication devices, will have effects on both the user and the family. The differences in family perceptions and values as compared to those of teachers in considering a device may be monumental. Some of these values are based on cultural differences.

For example, a family may be involved as members of a religious community. This family may want their child's device to be programmed with prayers so that the child can participate in their religious services. Perhaps the device only has a limited amount of memory and that is all dedicated to the prayers. Teachers may feel frustrated that the device cannot then be used for educational purposes and curricular themes.

Building an Effective Intervention Team

Probably more important than selecting exactly the right piece of equipment or the perfect augmentative system is providing sufficient support and collaboration for the individuals involved to ensure effective implementation of the device. Before the equipment is ordered, the report is finalized, and final decisions are announced, it is important to share information, ideas, concerns, and priorities to establish the joint ownership of this system and its use.

Numerous books have been written on the topic of teaming, collaboration, and interdisciplinary groups. Implementation teaming and roles are discussed in depth in Chapter 6, but briefly, we must mention some "teaming" information here.

One of the pitfalls of having an "evaluation team" separate from the "implementation team" is the possibility that the implementers will see the evaluators as the "experts." This perspective can result in the implementation team not taking the responsibility for programming and expanding the communication system but rather waiting for the "experts" to come back and tell them what to do next. Sometimes the technology that seems so familiar to the evaluation team appears overwhelmingly complex to the implementers. The "technology fear factor" of "losing everything" or "breaking" this expensive piece of equipment causes the device to be placed on a shelf and only taken out when the designated "professionals" are available. It is important for the evaluators to work to support the implementers and be willing to release the role of "professional" to those who are using the system with the communicator on a daily basis. These two roles need to be viewed as a symbiotic rather than a superior/subordinate relationship.

Establishing Team Participation

If the implementation team and evaluation team are different, initially the teams should meet to share the vision of how the system can be used, the possibilities the system possesses, and the initial targets for communication. One possible way to ensure team participation is to "brainstorm" ideas of communication targets for the individual from a group representative of all of the environments the individual encounters. Brainstorming involves taking all ideas presented without judging them as they are given and later going back to select the most desirable, workable ideas to implement first. An example of this type of brainstorming is outlined below.

With the team members present (e.g., evaluators, teachers, other caregivers, spouses, parents), take a large sheet of paper and begin your brainstorming session. List the target skills under each heading you select (e.g., home, restaurants, stores, academic classes, relatives' homes, friends). Begin by identifying a skill the individual is currently not using (e.g., responding to yes/no questions) and place this item under each heading where it is appropriate. Remember at this point, no ideas are out of bounds. The idea is to list as many

Brainstorming for Justin

Home
Answer yes/no questions
Follow directions
Ask for things he wants (e.g., videos, computer, TV)
Sit through dinner
Ask for help when he needs it

Restaurant
Order his own food
Ask for a drink refill
Answer yes/no questions
Occupy himself quietly until others finish
Ask for extra condiments, silverware, or even help when he needs it

Wal-Mart
Ask where the rest room is
Ask for an item
Tell me (before he explodes) that we need to leave
Accept limits on playing video games in the electronics section
Find items on a list (picture list?)
Produce identification when asked

School (classroom)
Answer yes/no questions
Ask for items/activities he wants
Accept "not now"
Use words to get a toy from another child
Sing morning songs and say the pledge

Ask for sensory inputs
Accept "no"
Understand "wait"

School (recess)
Respond when his name is called
Stop when directed on play equipment
Ask others if he can play in a game

ideas as you can in a specified time period. Once the ideas have been gathered, begin to determine targets for intervention. After sharing ideas about skills that may be emerging, consider by environment what skills in that setting might be expected of this individual over the next two to five years. Then, as a group, choose and prioritize which skills from the brainstorming list are most important to teach first for the communicator to promote independence, confidence, and effective results that will continue to motivate her to use the system in a broader range of interactions.

For individuals who have acquired an inability to speak (e.g., through neurological insult, disease, degeneration, or damage to the speech mechanism), it may be more appropriate to implement a long-term plan for use of the device since you can anticipate more sophisticated use based on the

The Life of Technology

Why address only the two-to-five-year spectrum? Although a system may continue to be functional over a much longer period of time than two to five years, this framework is used to address current technology needs. You do not want to purchase features beyond those anticipated as useful for the individual as they often increase the size, weight, and price of the system. Instead, recommending a device with appropriate but not excessive features will allow you to use the device initially, grow with the system, and eventually move to an upgraded system, based on documented success and growth and the need to expand the system to meet the communicator's needs. For individuals who are developing communication skills, especially children, this appears to be the most appropriate strategy. By the time you are ready to upgrade to the more sophisticated system, technology will have progressed and you will be able to choose from new features (those we can't even imagine!) or benefit from the reduced price of established technology.

individual's previous verbal language abilities. Typically these users acquire one system and use it throughout their lives, although minor changes in access may be needed as medical and physical conditions change.

Once the target skills have been prioritized, individuals should be chosen for implementation. If there are different members on the evaluation team than on the implementation team, transitional support is crucial. The implemen-tation team must be supported well enough to feel confident in using and expanding the device. This support may take many forms. There may be formal workshops and inservices by the augmentative communication evaluation team, assistive technologist, or even representatives from the manufacturer of the device selected. It is important that the implementation team feel enough familiarity and security with the device to expand its everyday use when the "experts" are gone.

Often explaining that devices are insured, that their memory is backed up and cannot be destroyed by errant key activations, and that technical glitches will occur is enough to support the team initially. However, in some instances, it is necessary to physically assist in the hands-on implementation of a device on a regular basis in the daily environment and gradually build confidence and skills in others. Time spent on these activities may be crucial to the eventual success of the device for the user. Allowing time to share ideas, select programming targets, and model implementation strategies may be the key to helping staff develop confidence and skills to promote language building with the device through everyday activities.

In the school setting, the support process can be especially overwhelming with large caseloads and a variety of clients using various technologies. However, time spent sharing the knowledge and expertise you develop will create a group of other knowledgeable persons who can assist other AAC communicators. For example, if you have trained the classroom teacher to act as the "point person" (i.e., the person in charge of the device in that setting who makes sure that it is charged up and that the programmed choices are pertinent to that child's learning environment), and next year the student will have a new teacher, you may be able to ask the current teacher to train and be a resource for the next year's teacher. This method often allows them to converse on a level of teacher to teacher, a more comfortable and familiar role for them.

Alternatively, if the parent has been the point person for programming and maintaining the device, he or she may be able to assist the next year's classroom teacher. Developing a network of "experts" in implementation within a building or school district allows them to call on one another to solve problems and brainstorm ideas when technology goes awry (as it will) or when the individual is not demonstrating skills previously achieved with the technology.

The amount of time spent in these activities and the frequency required to be effective will vary from situation to situation. Some implementation teams quickly "buy in" and understand the need for a variety of communicative opportunities to allow the new system user to demonstrate and expand her skills. Other teams require more instruction, guidance, support, reading materials, and modeling to navigate through the implementation and expansion of the language system. Initial time spent with these groups reaps rewards later on if they can apply the information they have learned to address a new student, new situation, or new device with independence and confidence.

At this point in the process, it is usually helpful to begin to determine "assignments" or responsibilities for the device and its use, maintenance, and programming. Sometimes this becomes the job of the parent; sometimes the designated point person is the teacher or speech-language pathologist (SLP). It may be that duties are shared (e.g., the SLP maintains the device, but the occupational therapist is responsible for addressing concerns about the mounts and switches needed to access the device). One person may also be designated as the liaison with the insurance company or funding source for addressing concerns and making the actual request.

Funding

If the evaluation has been completed and some type of equipment is recommended, it may be time to consider the funding sources available. Certain formats may be required by certain funding sources. If you anticipate submitting results to a particular funding source (e.g., Medicaid, private insurance, community organization), it is important to align your report to their format. If you generate a report that addresses all of their areas of concern, you will enhance your prospects of funding without protracted revisions and requests for more information. Often when dealing with funding agencies, you will be initially denied for some particular reason. If that particular issue is addressed through an addendum to the report, funding can sometimes be obtained. A different reviewer may see the request each time you submit to a funding source, so never give up until you have resubmitted a minimum of three times.

In some instances, manufacturers of equipment are willing to assist in the funding process. Contact the company and ask if they have a "funding information packet" or a funding specialist.

Equipment recommendations are generally written by features that are needed rather than by specific names of devices. Each feature listed should be addressed and supported in the report of the evaluation and trial periods. Most insurers require considering at least two systems that would meet the individual's needs as outlined on the feature-match list. A side-by-side comparison is often helpful, including the following:

- features (e.g., size, weight, voice quality)
- price
- manufacturers
- available technical and repair support
- training available from the manufacturer
- rental period availability
- warranty information
- accessories needed and included in the listed price

Features	Portable Impact Tablet Model	Dynamyte
Weight	2 lbs.	3.2 lbs.
Size	8.9"x 6.5"x 1.3"	8" x 7" x 2"
Screen Size	7.75" diagonal screen	6.5" diagonal, active matrix color
Screen Display Type	LCD	LCD
Resolution	640x480	640x480
Software	DEC Talk	DEC Talk
Memory Card	32MB expanded	16MB
Average Battery Life	6-8 hours (rechargeable)	5 hours continuous
Price	$3900 (device, case, external speaker, expanded memory card, and editing software)	$6395 (device) $50 (carrying case) $60 (back-up software)

Other examples of these lists can be found in the sample reports included in Appendix G on pages 157-170. Once the lists are generated, write a summary paragraph to explain why one device might be more desirable than another (if appropriate). Typically the insurer will select the less expensive device unless some extenuating circumstance exists that is outlined in this section.

Many times after the initial paperwork is submitted for insurance funding, the insurer will respond with a denial or a request for additional information/documentation of some aspect of the evaluation report. It is important to reply quickly and directly to the questions or concerns identified by the company. Frequently the policy will state a timeline (e.g., 30 days) in which appeals must be submitted in order to be considered for approval.

Some insurance companies will cover augmentative communication devices under "durable medical equipment" information. Speech devices are viewed as "voice prostheses." Much as an artificial limb aids a person in walking or grasping items, a voice-output device improves the person's functionality through communication.

Insurance policies may have a specific exclusion of augmentative communication devices or a specific limitation of only "non-computer based" devices. Looking at the wording in the insurance policy while writing the final draft of the report will help in selecting the proper vocabulary to increase the chances of funding.

Letters of Support

Letters of support from the individual's primary physician as well as therapists and caregivers are generally required for approval from a private insurance or Medicaid/Medicare provider. If a trial period has been conducted, the change in the ability of the individual to function, as well as any changes in affect, should be documented in support of the device. Often physicians are willing to support a device but lack the time and experience in drafting letters regarding communication devices. Providing a sample letter to a physician may help to streamline the process. A sample letter for a physician is included in Appendix H on page 171.

School District Funding Responsibilities

Under IDEA (1997), school districts have a responsibility to provide assistive technology for students who require such equipment to participate in the general curriculum. Certainly learning to speak and communicate fits under the learning standards of national, state, and local school organizations. Therefore, the school has an obligation to provide appropriate equipment for the student to use during their school years. The district may provide any piece of equipment that meets the specifications of the feature match list in the evaluation report, provided the need for that equipment is listed in the student's Individualized Education Plan (IEP). It is recommended that this equipment be listed by features (e.g., voice-output communication aid with at least 32 locations and scanning capabilities) rather than by brand name. If features are listed, a piece of lost, damaged, or broken equipment can be replaced with an equivalent alternative (in the case where the original model is not available) without holding an IEP review.

Whether the device is owned by the individual or the school district, if the equipment is used at school for school assignments and participation and listed on the IEP, the responsibility for repairs lies with the school district. Legally, the IEP team has determined this is a necessary piece of equipment needed for the child's environment, and the district must provide that assistive technology support.

Adult Funding Issues

Often the funding issues for adult onset users of augmentative communication systems can be quite different from those of young users. Depending on the nature of the condition that caused the loss of speech abilities and the prognosis, several options may be available to the individual.

Insurance funding may be an option. The same guidelines listed in the previous section for carefully reading and tailoring the report to meet the requirements of the insurance companies requests are important here. Documenting the medical necessity of this device to share with health care professionals how the client feels (physical and emotional) and thinks, and sometimes to convey legal information regarding the client's care, can all be reasonable justifications for an augmentative communication system.

Additionally, some support groups for particular disabilities, such as Amyotrophic Lateral Sclerosis (Lou Gehrig's disease) support groups, muscular dystrophy, and cerebral palsy, may have local support personnel or libraries of equipment that can be borrowed for a period of use (with or without rental fees) for use by patients. Private agencies, such as Elks, Optimists, Knights of Columbus, and other local civic groups, may also have loan or rental programs available or may be willing to provide at least partial funding to worthy causes. Some state assistive technology grants fund "exchange networks" where used equipment no longer needed is donated for use by others. Many of these are coordinated by the statewide assistive technology centers, such as the Assistive Technology Exchange Network (ATEN) in Illinois.

One other important factor for adults (and some children) is the progressive nature of their disabilities. If the course of the illness is known, the device selected might address not only current needs but anticipate future needs. For example, if a progressive neuromuscular disorder is known to affect the limb strength as part of its course, a person who may currently be able to use a device by direct selection may later need the scanning capability that a device can offer. Appropriate support in the report and the anticipation of ordering peripheral equipment (e.g., switches, mounts, wheelchair mounting systems) should be reflected in the report. It may not be appropriate to order the equipment at that time, as you may need to wait on the progression to determine where appropriate switch sites and types would be. This may depend on the motor abilities that remain when switches are implemented.

Conclusion

Often very little attention is paid to the portion of the process between the evaluation and the implementation. It is a necessary time to come together with a vision for the user and with cooperative efforts to secure funding and equipment. It is also a time to begin role release and sharing of knowledge with the user and support staff (Linder 1990). Parents and other caregivers should be integral parts of this bridging step to increase chances of successful implementation of the selected augmentative communication systems.

Intervention Strategies for Effective Communication

Intervention is the most critical part of effective communication with a device or other augmented communication means. There is no magic in a machine or picture system that transports individuals from the non-speaking world to the world of effective communication. Numerous factors must be considered and developed into strategies for successful implementation.

In this chapter we will discuss the following:

- changes needed in the physical environment for the communication system user

- selection and use of appropriate vocabulary

Adaptations and modifications may need to be made in the home, school, and community to establish the communication system for the user. Some teachers and caregivers may question the changes to the environment needed just to facilitate the use of the device. It is important to remember that this is an initial training phase. It might be compared to teaching 16-year-olds to drive. They have seen others drive for years and anticipated their own opportunity to do likewise, but we don't just hand over the keys at age 16. We provide simulators and we study about driving in a manner different from how they have thought or discussed in the past. We give them many hours of practice sessions with a "back up" (a right-sided brake on the driver's education vehicles). We even mark their cars with huge yellow signs on the top to let people know that something different is coming down the road toward them.

Similarly, for the new communicator to be successful, we must create some of those same learning opportunities and experiences and ask those in the environment to adjust to this new user. We have to begin with that "obstacle course in the parking lot" before moving to the "interstate." And, much like driving, some users will learn faster than others and some will always be better users than others.

The Physical Environment: Mounting vs. Portability

There are several factors to consider in the use of a device or picture system for the user. The first factor is whether the user of the system walks independently or requires a wheelchair or walker to move from place to place. If the individual is primarily in a wheelchair, the device or picture system can be attached or mounted to his wheelchair system to provide access to the device whenever he is in his chair.

Mounting systems vary by manufacturers. Assuming the individual is receiving an augmentative communication device, the system will need to be attached to the wheelchair for the individual to have access. It is important that the caregivers responsible for attaching the device initially check to ensure the mounting system is operating correctly. Eventually they can teach the user to perform the check independently if he is capable.

Device Mounting Considerations

- screen location
- mounting security
- adding to wheelchair dimensions
- using device mounts during transport

Screen Location

If the user is activating the device by direct selection (e.g., touching with finger, using a headpointer), it is essential that the distance from the user to the device accommodate that access modality. Also, if the individual is able to independently maneuver his wheelchair, the device may need to be placed slightly higher or lower on his wheelchair to allow for unobstructed vision as he moves about.

Mounting Security

Consideration must be given to where the device is mounted onto the wheelchair. Device brackets are generally attached to the mainframe of the wheelchair. It can be tempting to mount a device on the footrest or arm support due to ease of mounting, but these places are not recommended. The chair is less strong and less rigid there and is not stable enough for the device. There is also an increased chance of damage if the device falls, not to mention excessive wear and tear on the wheelchair itself.

Adding to Wheelchair Dimensions

Any equipment added to the wheelchair will generally increase its dimensions in some way. Positioning devices and switches on the sides of the wheelchair may make the wheelchair too wide for the individual to maneuver through doorways and aisles. Therefore, try to limit the width you add to the wheelchair.

Using Device Mounts During Transport

This issue is cause for controversy and concern in many school districts. Depending on the type of mounting system, the type of restraints used on the bus, and whether the individual rides the bus in the wheelchair or sits in an adapted seat on the bus are all issues to consider. Student safety is paramount. Generally these decisions are made individually by the team members or by a transportation coordinator who has the experience, insight, and/or resources for making these decisions. If the device cannot be safely mounted during transport, an alternative low-tech system may need to be used to meet the passenger's communication needs as he travels.

These same issues (e.g., mounting security, impact of width on the chair, safety in transport) must be considered with any switch mounts the user needs to access his device. Each time the switch mounts are removed, adjusted, or reattached, location and positioning of switches should be checked to ensure that they are accessible and working properly with the communication system.

Sometimes a device may be placed on the laptray of a wheelchair for user access. If there is excessive pressure or activity in the daily situation, it may be a good idea to place a nonslip material on the laptray prior to placing the device there. Occupational therapists might use Dycem for this purpose. Rubberized shelf-lining paper available at discount department stores may also work.

Transport Considerations

If the individual walks independently or with an assistive device (e.g., cane, walker, crutches), then it is necessary to determine how to transport the communication device from one location to another. Initially, the staff may transport the device for the individual, but eventually some method of transport should be established that allows the user to move it with him.

In some cases, a pushcart may be appropriate. Devised as a simple top and bottom box on wheels, a pushcart can provide a means for moving books and backpacks as well as a place for storing the device so it is accessible while walking down the hall. The frame can also be adjusted to an appropriate height to stabilize the individual as he is walking. The custodian, carpentry staff, or shop class may be able to make this type of cart. If these resources are not available, there are a number of commercially-produced carts of this type that can be purchased. Of course another means of transport must be found if the school or building is on more than one level without elevators or ramps, or if the ramps are too steep for the user to navigate with a cart independently.

Other individuals with communication devices who are ambulatory may use a strap or carrying case to use the device while in transit from one place to another. If this is the plan, it is important to ensure that the individual is able to manage the weight and design of the device to avoid getting thrown off balance.

Some devices, especially those with dynamic screens, may be difficult to use in natural light or may require adjustments to the screen between environments in the school. Again, it is the responsibility of the caregivers initially to make these adjustments and then to teach the user to change them if he is able, or at least to ask for assistance.

Regardless of whether the device is mounted, carried, pushed, or moved in other ways, the bottom line is that if the device is not available to the user when opportunities to communicate arise, he will not be able to use it. Also, extra support and guidance is required in the initial stages, but the goal is to move the user to independence in accessing the device across environments to the extent possible.

Selection and Use of Appropriate Communication Targets

Before placing the device with the user, several decisions need to be addressed. One of the first is "What should be on the device?" or, in the case of the device that arrives with a great deal of messages and boards already developed, "How will we teach this vocabulary and what should we teach first?" The level of communication may be determined by what you already know of the individual from the evaluation. During the transition phase, the team should have brainstormed and prioritized ideas for communication use and targets. Now, at the implementation phase, the entire picture begins to coalesce.

- reviewing the ecological survey

- gathering baseline data

- selecting the vocabulary

- scripting

- strategies for teaching vocabulary

- using prompts for communication support

- addressing behavioral concerns

- strategies for specific populations

·74·

Reviewing the Ecological Survey

In Chapter 3 it is recommended that an ecological survey be conducted as part of the evaluation process. This documentation of missed communication opportunities for the user is an ongoing process throughout the implementation and expansion of a communication system. If you have not completed this survey yet, now is the time to begin.

It is often easy to spot the daily rituals that require a reply in a given setting (e.g., Are you buying lunch today or packing? What is the weather today?). By observing routine activities and noting questions asked to the group of peers, this needed vocabulary becomes the obvious data pool for selecting the vocabulary to teach to encourage daily use.

Typically teachers begin using the device at snack time and calendar time, but we often fail to identify social situations where the device user can take the lead and initiate the conversation. These situations may include greetings and requests for items or actions without being asked "What do you want?" Specific examples and strategies are identified under each of the user areas in this chapter, pages 82-115, but the concept of teaching spontaneous initiation is an integral piece. It should not be minimized in its importance in helping the user become an independent, functioning communicator.

Gathering Baseline Data

Although data collection is not generally a favorite activity of clinicians, teachers, or other caregivers, it is needed to monitor progress, chart usage, plan activities and strategies, and expand the vocabulary and activities available through a communication system. The value of data collection, however, is no better than the information you collect. Therefore, by determining the purpose of your data collection, you can be assured that you are collecting appropriate data for decision making.

If an individual is to become an effective communicator, he must communicate frequently. Practicing communication is no different than practicing a basketball shot—the more you do it, the more your accuracy and your ability to adjust to game situations will improve. For example, at the beginning phases of the Picture Exchange Communication training (Phase I), Frost & Bondy (1994) recommend at least 30 trials of picture exchange with more trials per day in the phases that follow. When you consider the number of conversational turns competent communicators use each day, the importance of numerous opportunities throughout the day becomes apparent.

Important data to collect is the number of times the individual accesses a communication system during a specified time period. That time may be a two-hour block, a school day, or a 24-hour period, depending on the user, the lifestyle, and the data you wish to gather. If results indicate periods of high use and a period of no use, the team should address possible barriers to communication affecting the user in the latter environment (e.g., positioning, vocabulary needed, teaching style).

·75·

In addition to this quantitative data, you may wish to gather qualitative data about the communicator. For example, if you believe that the communication device user needs to increase initiations, it is important to document how many initiations he makes during a day in order to establish an appropriate target. You may want to actually create a combined data collection/ecological survey form for a given skill where you can document where and when initiations occurred, and note times when an initiation would have been appropriate but the opportunity was missed. The number of different messages he uses, the number of initiations (as opposed to responses), and the types of messages (e.g., social greetings vs. requests to have needs/wants met) may provide information to consider in broadening his skills, vocabulary, and use of the device. The ecological survey type of information can reveal where the system is used most efficiently. You may also want to chart patterns of activations (e.g., Is the user always accessing the same square, always activating the scan after the third item is heard?, etc.) and analyze the patterns to determine that the user's activations are valid communications.

Be aware that not all team members are able to listen and understand concepts in the same way. Therefore, as you share data collection results with the team and plan future intervention targets, document information in several ways. Provide a verbal summary of the data, a written composite, and a visual chart or graph to demonstrate the current levels, target levels, and growth toward the goal. Continued work with a person using an augmentative device to expand his repertoire is a task that requires constant motivation not only for the user but also for the team. Even an experienced team can "stagnate" after successfully reaching a singular skill such as requesting, and fail to meet the additional needs of the communicator.

Selecting the Vocabulary

Currently there is ongoing research regarding whether devices should be programmed with single words or stored with phrases to improve communication. The obvious trade-off is speed of response as opposed to the ability to generate novel utterances to address new situations. This is a current area of research, and the question posed is how to devise the best blend for each individual user (Higginbotham 2001).

Using the ecological survey you have completed and the evaluative information you collected as guidelines, the next step is to select vocabulary that addresses pertinent social, academic, medical, and life skill areas for the user. Vocabulary to program will differ, depending on the user and the intent. For example, if you are working with a very young user and the goal is to develop language skills, you may program one button that says "I want" and another that says "I like" along with other items on the device. The intent of this programming would be that the child will move from one-word comments and requests (simply stating the item name) to combining the carrier phrase ("I want" or "I like") with the item name as he moves from one-word to two-word utterances developmentally.

Conversely, if the user is an adult with challenging access and limited communication abilities following some type of brain injury or insult, a phrase-based communication may allow him to convey messages more quickly, easily, and accurately. Although some skills may eventually be regained and the system may be changed later, the immediate need is for efficient communication of wants and needs. Adding vocabulary at a later time to meet expanded communication needs would be an important consideration depending on the course of the user's recovery.

Scripting

Scripting is a strategy in which a specific rather than general set of vocabulary is created to address the communication needs of beginning communicators, especially those with cognitive challenges (Elder & Goosens 1994). Scripts then are made up of words or phrases that relate to a specific activity.

Creating an Overlay for an Activity

By anticipating the types of interactions an activity will demand, appropriate scripts of words or phrases can be developed and used with an overlay or activity board to help the individual communicate in specific situations. Scripting is most successful with routine activities like morning circle, picking up attendance forms, cooking activities, checking out a library book, ordering at a restaurant or cafeteria, dressing, or social gatherings.

Regardless of the type of communication system (e.g., pictures, voice-output device, static or dynamic display), the overlay should reflect the vocabulary needed for a specific activity. The number of choices to present depends on the activity as well as the cognitive and motoric abilities of the individual. However, you need to include enough vocabulary options for the communicator to be a functional part of the experience. For example, an overlay for cooking activities in class may look like the following.

The Picture Communication Symbols © 1981-2002 Mayer-Johnson, Inc. Used with permission.

Selecting the Vocabulary to Program for the Script

The next decision is whether to store phrases or single word messages under each location. The ultimate decision is an individual one, generally based on the cognitive abilities of the communicator and the communication goals. The trade-off between these systems is speed vs. flexibility of the message generated (Elder & Goosens 1996).

Each system has advantages and disadvantages for the user. With a single word-based system, the user is able to generate novel utterances by combining single words. The user can use the vocabulary to create different meanings by selecting different word orders and expanding the number of words that are connected to produce a phrase. Unfortunately, the speed of the message is significantly slower with the single word system than with the phrase-based system. On the other hand, if phrases are stored beneath each icon, communication is less flexible as the user cannot alter the message content to meet varying communicative needs.

Home/School Communication

A simple beginning strategy to encourage use of the augmentative communication device and improve home/school communication involves a daily message. This message can be programmed into a particular location on the user's device or on a smaller, single-message device (e.g., a key chain type messager, single-switch message, or even a "talking photograph" type device available in stationery stores) that travels between home and school.

At the end of the day, a member of the child's team takes responsibility for programming in the answer to the daily question "What did you do at school today?" The staff member programs the message from the user's point of view. For example:

> "Today Miss Mary came for music and we got to go to the computer lab and play
> games. Lunch was vegetable soup and peanut butter sandwiches. YUCK!"

At home, before the child returns to school the following day, the parent programs the home message to answer the teacher's query, "What did you do last night?" Again, the response is recorded from the user's point of view. This response may be:

> "Last night we ate out at McDonald's and went to look at new kitchen cabinets.

This strategy encourages daily communication and increased expectations of use, as well as helps those at school and home become more comfortable programming the device. It functions as a check that both school and home are involved in communicating with the individual and ensures at least some level of augmented communication daily. In selecting the message to send back and forth, the daytime caregivers as well as the home personnel must consider what the quality of the user's day (or evening) has been like. Was he able to make choices about the events he participated in? Did he find those events enjoyable? Was he part of the action or did he simply tag along? Working with daily messages can encourage caregivers to examine quality of life issues involving recreational and leisure time, interest in structured activities presented, and preferences of the individual using the device.

Strategies for Teaching Vocabulary

Helping a new user find vocabulary and use his device in opportunities that arise is an important teaching task. Sometimes when teachers and therapists are beginning to teach vocabulary, there is a tendency to play "show me." In this game, the communication partner identifies the 10 or 15 vocabulary words she wants to teach. Then the communication partner says, "Find _____." In this out-of-context teaching situation, the goal becomes finding the word rather than transmitting a message. Once taught in this way, many communication device users have difficulty breaking out of the responding mode. They have trouble understanding that they can also use the newly learned vocabulary to initiate communication.

Instead of the "find this" strategy, a more appropriate implementation strategy is to give the user a reason to communicate, and then to teach the location of the vocabulary on the device. For example, if you have a user with significantly better receptive than expressive vocabulary skills, you may want to teach the location of emotion words. Your lesson could involve short one- or two-sentence descriptions of emotion provoking situations. For example, "When Joanie saw that her little brother had used markers all over the teddy bear that her boyfriend Jack had given her, steam began to come out of her ears." Then ask, "How do you think Joanie was feeling?" and present two vocabulary cards to cue the location of the emotion words (e.g., happy, mad) in the device.

The more complex the device, the more there may be a need for cue cards. For instance, in the Unity program used by many of the devices manufactured by the Prentke-Romich Company, the sequence for a feeling always begins with the icon with two masked faces. Then there are a several choices in the activity row that indicate a variety of emotions. The cue card would have a picture of the icon for the masked faces and each of the possibilities listed on it to help the user navigate and learn the "language" of the device and where specific items are stored.

Another example might involve a class discussion after reading a story. The individual with the augmentative communication system could be given cue cards to ask questions about the story and then select the class members to call on to answer the questions. For instance, if the child is included in a third-grade class reading *Charlotte's Web*, questions could revolve around character names or attributes, and the cue cards could pose specific questions based on content. The user could also be provided with other cue cards for any new vocabulary specific to this activity.

In any event, using the communication device to make choices, ask questions, or direct others is much more powerful in teaching and learning vocabulary than the "find this" method referred to on page 79.

Using Prompts for Communication Support

Selecting appropriate methods for prompting and cueing the individual with the communication device is important for successful implementation. The method of prompting and cueing used for the beginning communicator should be the least intrusive method that is successful, and the goal of removing all prompts and cues for movement toward independence should never be forgotten.

Intrusive prompts are those that interfere with communication. Just as children are taught not to interrupt when adults are trying to communicate, it follows that verbal prompts interrupt the flow of a conversation between a device user and his partner much more than a touch cue, light cue, or waiting to see if the user can access the vocabulary independently. Bondy (1996) recommends selecting a variety of prompting strategies with the eventual goal to eliminate all prompts so that the individual functions independently.

Types of Prompts

- verbal
- gestural
- physical
- light cueing

Prompting strategies may include verbal, gestural, physical, and light cueing prompts. Verbal prompts are often used but can be highly intrusive and difficult to fade. A new user may require verbal prompts initially to attend to his device and to learn new vocabulary. Ideally, these prompts will be paired with less intrusive prompts, such as a tap on the device, and eventually the verbal prompt can be faded and the less intrusive gestural prompt will replace it. Less invasive strategies, such as gestural (e.g., pointing, tapping) and physical prompts (e.g., a touch on the shoulder or the hand to cue the user to respond), may provide adequate levels of support to accomplish the interaction without excessive prompting. If the goal is independent communication, all prompts must eventually be removed. This goal can be most effectively accomplished if all communicative partners for the individual are moving through this hierarchy of prompts in the same way, prompting with the same technique, and working to reduce the intrusiveness of prompts and cues as vocabulary knowledge and user participation increases.

Aided Language Stimulation is a facilitation technique in which the facilitator uses a light (e.g., a penlight or small flashlight) to highlight specific areas on the individual's device or overlay during the interaction to cue the target response (Elder and Goosens 1996). There are three stages of light cueing identified in this hierarchy.

- Constant or flashing light cue—Place the light on the symbol to be selected and either hold it constantly on, or flash the light on and off on the target location.

- Pause/momentary light cue—Insert a pause prior to cueing with the light to stimulate a response, and then cue if needed; often this cue is produced and then removed once the user sees the target but before he accesses the targeted button.

- Prompt hierarchy (combination of search light cueing, momentary light cueing, and constant light cueing)—Searchlight cueing involves a sweeping motion over the area of the location without specifically stopping on the targeted location, much like a searchlight sweeps the sky. This is a more general level of cueing, and if it is not successful in generating the target response, the momentary light cue or the constant or flashing light cue is used instead.

Using a penlight to cue is much less intrusive than physical pointing or gesturing to the appropriate selection. Additionally, if you are pointing at the correct response with your finger, the symbol is actually out of view of the user because your finger is covering it.

Various light sources can be used for light cueing techniques. The most popular are the squeezeable lights or a penlight, each of which can be worn on a chain around the prompter's neck, ready to use whenever it is needed in the functional classroom setting.

Addressing Behavioral Concerns

Often individuals who have limited communication problems also have coexisting behavior problems. Individuals with developmental delays, those with autism, and sometimes young children with apraxia or other difficulties that limit their ability to interact with others and control their surroundings will act out against themselves, others, or their environment to express themselves. Typically this behavior serves a purpose for the individual who displays it and must be analyzed and replaced with a more socially acceptable communication. The new communication must be reinforced over a variety of different people, places, times, and situations if it is to become a habit (Carr et al. 1994).

Complete texts have been written on effectively teaching communication strategies to promote pro-social behaviors. It is beyond the scope of this text to address the wide range of behavioral issues, but the implementation team should be aware that behavioral concerns can and will arise. These behavior problems may indicate frustration with the communication system. Sometimes problem behaviors may be used for more than one purpose. For example, if we determine that Johnny pinches because he can't ask for the snack he wants, we address that behavior through a communication system. We may find that although Johnny pinches less, he still continues to pinch. It may be that the behavior (pinching) was also serving as a release for his need for deep sensory input or to gain the attention of an adult. If the behavior continues after the child has learned an alternate behavior, we need to continue to develop hypotheses as to the functions of the behavior and develop additional communication skills/methods to address those needs.

Strategies for Specific Populations

Unfortunately, there is no cookbook for augmentative communication intervention. In the remainder of this chapter, intervention issues, strategies, target skills, systems, and case studies are presented for a variety of communicators.

- individual with severe developmental delays and motor difficulties

- individual with autism/PDD and significant behavioral problems

- individual with mild cognitive impairments and/or mild motor involvement

- adult with acquired speech disabilities

No "profile" of an individual could address all of the extenuating circumstances and background information. Each case is different and should be considered as such. Principles can be learned and taught, but remember that augmentative communication evaluation and implementation is as much an art as it is science. Be ready to create, test, and prove your hypotheses each day, and be willing to revise your plans as circumstances dictate.

Individual with Severe Developmental Delays & Motor Difficulties

Intervention Issues

1. Access/motor capabilities

For individuals with severe physical disabilities, access to the communication device and the availability of the system throughout the day is paramount. These individuals need the systems to be close by and set up for them (e.g., mounted, turned on, switch placement secured) if they are to use their systems effectively.

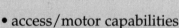

- access/motor capabilities
- behavior
- reinforcers
- cognitive issues
- staff/caregiver training

Another consideration involves changing of positions during the day and providing access to the augmentative communication device not only in the wheelchair, but also in the stander, on the floor mat, and at the lunch table in a modified seat. Each move may require a different setup in order for the user to successfully communicate in that environment. It is important to keep in mind that when an individual with significant motor and cognitive challenges learns a new motor movement or position to activate the device, it is often like learning an entirely new skill and can take a significant amount of time.

2. Behavior

Many times individuals with significant developmental delays have used behavioral methods to signal others to meet their needs, and switching to communication different from their current ways may be difficult. Just as we don't communicate through any single method, we should not expect those who use augmentative communication to be limited to their devices.

If a communicator has a signal that works and is understood by the majority of people (e.g., head shake and nod for "no" and "yes"), there is little reason to replace it on the device. You can also use signals the individual has (e.g., pointing at a desired object) to expand communication. Select often-requested items to represent in pictures on the device. Begin to help the user learn the symbol representation for a desired object by pairing the device activation and the presentation of the reinforcing item. Eventually, as the connection becomes stronger, the user realizes that he can even request items out of sight by using the device and activating that location. Being able to control the environment in this way is typically a powerful reinforcer for the user.

If a communicator is using a challenging or self-abusive behavior to communicate (e.g., screaming or hitting himself when the environment becomes too noisy), the device may offer an excellent alternative strategy to meet the need that the behavior currently addresses. If the source can be identified, a message can be programmed to address the needs of the individual (e.g., "It's too loud. I'd like to go out of the room."). The key to promoting a change in the behavior pattern is to do a thorough functional analysis and establish a functional alternative, using a strong reinforcement schedule. If assistance is needed in analyzing behaviors, appropriate resources may be the behavior consultant or the psychologist.

Functional Analysis

- target behavior
- current intensity, frequency, or duration
- setting for the behavior (place, time, persons)
- antecedent (what triggers the behavior)
- consequence (what the individual gains from the behavior)
- function (what appears to be the purpose of the behavior/is it communicative?)
- modifications (what modifications have been attempted to address the behavior)
- alternate behaviors (what the individual could do instead)

3. Reinforcers

To create interest in communication for individuals with significant cognitive challenges, it is important to know what they like and enjoy. It is logical that individuals will "work" to communicate if they are properly reinforced, whether that is listening to their favorite music or receiving a backrub. To create a list of reinforcers for an individual, observe and ask other caregivers what the individual truly enjoys and looks forward to each day, and choose that as a beginning reinforcer for communication.

A speech-language pathologist servicing students with significant developmental delays shared the following insight.

"I rarely have parents 'overjoyed' at the news that a device will be introduced. I think it causes them to grieve the 'loss' of verbal speech. I've had several cry and ask 'Will he/she ever talk?' Others say 'There's no time' or 'I already understand my child.' Although I always come to the team meetings very excited about beginning a device, I realize that the parent may not feel the same. Parents need time to accept the change. I have found the best strategy for getting families 'on board' is to get the child at least semi-proficient with the device at school, and then have the parents come observe or send home a video. A home visit and ecological study are important follow-up.

Limiting caregiver obligation by just asking them to use it one or two times over the weekend sometimes works to get things going at home. Also using the ecological study to come up with things the child cannot communicate to the family may be helpful.
(Personal correspondence 2002)

4. Cognitive Issues

Determining cognitive level prior to implementation of a communication system is often difficult because the individual has no way to demonstrate or express what he knows, especially if he demonstrates significant motor challenges that limit his ability to participate in manipulative tasks (e.g., creating block designs, pointing, matching, sorting). With the introduction of a communication system or environmental control system, the user finally can demonstrate some of his skills in cause/effect and means/end. With this information, the team becomes responsible to encourage the user to demonstrate more of his cognitive abilities and to challenge him to expand his communication skills.

You can create learning opportunities for more advanced cognitive skills using the techniques of scaffolding, expanding, or previewing, according to the individual's abilities and interests. For example, a child with motoric limitations cannot manipulate toys with his hands, but he can learn to match and name colors through electronic means.

5. Staff/caregiver training

One of the important steps in implementation for this population is ensuring that the individual's caregiver shares the vision of the augmentative communication plan. Often the caregiver understands and anticipates the needs of the person and is so genuinely concerned about the individual's welfare and comfort that she meets the individual's needs even before the individual communicates what he wants. The caregiver needs to learn to wait for the individual to make a communicative attempt toward the specified targets before presenting the reinforcement.

Despite the fact that augmentative communication, in the minds of the evaluation and implementation teams, opens avenues of communication to non-speaking individuals, caregivers may not be as receptive to this technology initially. They are often concerned that the professional staff is "giving up" on verbal speech production and feel yet another sense of "loss" about their loved one. Parents and caregivers need to be educated about the need to develop language skills even if speech production is not continuing. They need to also be aware that there is no evidence showing that introduction of augmentative communication systems impedes speech production, but rather there are studies to the contrary on this point (Goosens 1989). If the caregivers are hesitant to use the device at home but do not object to classroom use, begin there. One way to promote the use of technology at home is to have the individual use it to communicate items that he could not understand previously.

Care providers may need specific training and modeling to understand how to wait and reinforce as this will be a different behavior for many of them. They may need help understanding that by waiting, they will begin to promote independence and communication in the individual, and that they will be assisting in his life-long learning. Once the caregivers perceive that they help the individual more by waiting than by doing, they become some of the best implementers in the environment because of the amount of one-on-one time they typically have with the user.

Strategies

1. Reinforcement inventory

It is necessary to determine objects and activities that the individual enjoys to motivate him to participate in the activity. Observing what the person enjoys, asking caregivers questions, and/or presenting a variety of stimuli for each of the senses to determine preferences and reactions are all ways of determining what the individual may enjoy.

- reinforcement inventory
- establishing an access mode
- symbol associations
- replacing behaviors with alternate communications

Some individuals will attempt to direct or control their larger environments (e.g., the entire classroom), but others will choose to impact only their own corner of the world. For example, the user may enjoy controlling music on a headset but not enjoy turning on music for the entire class. Another individual may be willing to activate a switch to pour the cereal into his bowl, but he won't participate in group cooking activities by pouring ingredients into the mixing bowl. For these reasons, especially in cases where defining reinforcers is difficult, it may be beneficial to include specifics of contexts and activities that the individual preferred.

2. Establishing an access mode

Each user must have some way to access his choice (e.g., use of a switch, eye-gaze system, selecting and giving a picture). The access system may have been established in the evaluation section but during the implementation phase, it is not unusual for the team to determine that different situations may require different access systems, depending on the positioning of the individual. Positioning often affects strength and range of motion available for activating communication devices and/or switches.

3. Symbol associations

Once you have established the inventory of reinforcers and have identified several items that the user would enjoy, you can begin to establish beginning communication by matching symbol associations with the desired reinforcers. Symbols often bear a tangible relationship to the requested activity or item. For example, the symbol could be a small replica (e.g., a doll rocking chair to indicate he would like to be rocked) or an item with a similar texture or feel to his request (e.g., a small fuzzy square of the same material as his favorite naptime blanket).

One carryover strategy may be to remove the object from a box or shelf where the picture is located to begin an object-picture association for the user. This strategy may take an amount of teaching time but will benefit the user. Initially present both the picture and the item. For example, to help a child request a snack, the first step is to take a spoon out of a box labeled with a picture of a spoon. Ultimately, the child will touch or pass the picture of the spoon instead of using the actual object to request a snack. Picture use is preferred as communication is more portable and useful across environments with the use of pictures than with objects.

4. Replacing behaviors with alternate communications

Once the functional analysis of the behavior has been conducted, it is best for the team to select one or two top priorities for intervention from the behavior realm. If the functional analysis has been successful, you have established the goal of the behavior and what the individual is trying to communicate via that undesired behavior.

Team intervention is imperative to reduce/eliminate negative behaviors. Given what you know about the user, provide a communication option in the moments prior to the onset of the negative behavior. This option will interrupt the cycle, give the user the desired outcome, and encourage him to learn a new more acceptable refusal behavior for the current negative behavior.

For example, the functional analysis indicates that the student consistently screams whenever music is presented in the classroom situation, but the student tolerates music in other situations. It is perceived that the function of the behavior is to avoid changing to another activity because the student associates music in the classroom with a change of activity/positioning that occurs on a regular basis throughout the day. Given this information, the staff begins to create a tactile schedule (i.e., a series of textured items) to help the student understand what activity he will participate in next. For puzzles, he may be given a piece of a puzzle; when it is naptime, he receives a piece of cloth that resembles his blanket; and when it is time to go outside, he is given a small rock to represent the playground stones. This predictability lets the student know what is next and reduces the anxiety of transitioning between activities. By assisting the student in anticipating the next event through touch and a "counting down" technique (e.g., either using a visual timer or telling the student "just 3 more minutes," "just two more minutes," "one more minute, then we change," etc.), the negative behavior cycle regarding transitions may be significantly reduced or eliminated.

Target Skills

1. Cause/effect

If a child does not understand cause and effect, it will be very difficult to develop further communication skills. At one time, interventionists and evaluators would simply report the child was "not ready" for communication. Today, however, it is believed that if the child has not developed this skill independently, then the implementation team should attempt to teach it.

- cause/effect
- turn taking
- requesting an object or action

In teaching this skill, you may initially need to "cause" the child to touch the symbolic representation with "hand-over-hand" assistance or by moving the symbol to touch the child's hand. The reinforcer should then be presented within three seconds so the child can make the connection between performing the access behavior (e.g., touching the item presented, activating the switch, looking at the item) and receiving the reinforcer (Korsten et al. 1993). When there is another opportunity for the reinforcer, present the symbol or switch again to elicit (hopefully) an independent response to gain the reinforcer. It may take an extended number of trials and experiences to solidify the cause/effect skill. Also a higher level of prompting may be required initially, but as always, the goal is to decrease the prompting to encourage independent participation.

2. Turn taking

Turn taking is one of the early nonverbal communication skills young children demonstrate. If a child has failed to develop turn taking in nonverbal activities, it will be difficult to teach him to participate in verbal turn taking. Verbal communication relies on symbolic constructs much more abstract than the nonverbal turn taking in early infancy.

When an individual is just beginning to use a device, he might initiate without understanding "what" the communication is, but he will learn to initiate and take a turn by the response he gets. For example, if a single-message switch is placed on a child's laptray with the message "Come and give me a big hug," the message will be reinforced by the caregivers in the area. Once the communication is begun, the caregiver can wait expectantly for the device user to activate the switch again, either for the same message or (if a multi-step message button is used) to make the next request.

3. Requesting an object or action

This skill may begin as simply touching the symbol presented. After this response is established on several items, you may begin to offer a choice of two items for the user to choose from, using whatever access mode you have selected.

If the user fails to make accurate discriminations or you are unsure from the individual's response whether the item selected was the item desired, revise the choice making protocol to include an intermediate step between one choice and two choices. This step would either include choosing between a preferred and non-preferred choice, or choosing between a desired item and a blank choice. If the data on the selections made by the individual indicate there is only a chance probability he is selecting accurately, further work on discrimination must be completed prior to moving on (Frost & Bondy 1994). Interventions to correct discrimination problems may include changing the stimulus (e.g., from photographs to line drawings or symbols, from visual to tactile choices, from visual to auditory selections, pairing two modalities for selections) to increase the success rate.

Systems

1. Symbol associations

As stated previously, symbol associations may be miniatures of actual choices, materials that represent the choice, or articles related to the choice (e.g., spoon for eating). Most often these are not commercially available products but rather a unique set of materials collected over time and individualized for the person using the device.

Some individuals who use augmented communication will begin at this level and move to more abstract symbols, but others will require this level of concrete association for all communication. Carefully document and maintain records of symbols explored, initiated, understood, and used on the communication log (See sample on page 40) as these will be important records for the next caregiver who will need to communicate with the individual. Without such records, each new caregiver will have to "reinvent the wheel."

Systems

- symbol associations
- single-message switches
- multi-step single switches
- environmental control unit (ECU)
- pictures (eye-gaze or picture exchange)
- anticipation shelves

2. Single-message switches

Single-message switches are commercially available. Companies such as AbleNet and Enabling Devices offer a variety of sizes to accommodate a wide range of motoric abilities. Bear in mind that the smaller the switch the individual can accurately target, the more targets you can provide within the user's range of motion.

3. Multi-step single switches

Multi-step single switches are also commercially available and provide an opportunity for scripting sequences. All that is required of the user is that he activate the switch, wait for a response from the communication partner, and activate the switch again. In the example below, the "switch vocabulary" is indicated in bold text and the "communicative partner" in the plain text.

Hi! My name is Jessica. What's yours?

I'm Mrs. Cavins.

I love cookies, don't you?

Well, yes, I do like cookies.

Well, you're in luck. My Girl Scout troop is selling them right now. The order form is this folder.

Oh, my . . . I don't know.

We don't need the money today. Just mark the boxes you'd like and I'll be back to deliver them in March.

Well, okay. I guess I'll buy two boxes.

Thank you. I hope you have a great day!

Initially when introducing such strategies, it is important to tell communication partners to be ready in case something should "go wrong" (e.g., a double activation or an unclear message). However, over time, these scripts can be used independently by the communicator for a variety of routine tasks. It's important to think through potential responses by the communication partner in order to program the device so the person using it can respond appropriately. For example, even if the respondent above didn't order cookies, it would still be appropriate to say "thank you" at the end of the interaction. If the programmed statement were "thank you for your order" and the individual had not placed an order, the communication would have seemed less appropriate and the communication more awkward.

This scripting strategy for a multi-step switch has proved beneficial even with high school students to increase their appreciation of communicating with others. Once scripts have been established and used, you may wish to keep a log of the scripts in a notebook so the individual can choose to repeat a particular script if desired (e.g., jokes, sports comments, personal events).

4. Environmental control unit (ECU)

ECUs are commercially available in both wired and wireless formats. They are excellent tools for teaching cause and effect, and also wonderful ways to allow individuals to participate in group activities. An ECU works as an interceptor between an electrical device (e.g., blender, toaster, boom box) and an individual's switch. The ECU is plugged into the wall, and the user's switch and the appliance are plugged into the ECU. By adjusting settings on the ECU, the user's switch can perform in a number of different ways.

- Latching—Touch the switch once to turn the appliance on, and a second time to disengage the appliance.

- Timer—Touch the switch once to turn the appliance on. When the timer expires, the appliance turns off. Touch the switch again to restart the appliance.

- Direct—Touch and hold the switch to run the appliance. When you let go of the switch, the appliance stops.

Depending on the skill you are trying to teach and the activity presented, either mode described below may prove useful:

- pictures (eye gaze or picture exchange)

- anticipation shelves

Pictures (eye gaze or picture exchange)

If a person who uses augmentative communication has the ability to pick up pictures or symbols, an exchange system where the individual can initiate interactions may be beneficial. An interaction requires both a speaker (initiator) and a receiver (responder). Often caring individuals ask those who do not speak many questions that can be answered by "yes" or "no" in attempts to understand what they want and what they know. This behavior causes the individual to develop excellent responding skills but not initiating skills. Most AAC users begin as responders with their devices because they don't know where the information is stored and they have such limited experience initiating an interaction. Initiating a request or a conversational exchange is often a skill that needs to be taught. If the user does not learn to initiate interactions, he will always depend on others and his level of independence will be compromised.

If the user is cognitively challenged or is using an eye-gaze system, a vast number of choices may be overwhelming and difficult to manage. Perhaps the individual cannot discriminate among a field of pictures greater than four, or using eye gaze is difficult when he moves beyond four locations. In this case, the first choice for this user may be the category of reinforcer that he wants (e.g., something to eat; something to play with; a sensory reinforcer, like vibration or deep pressure). After the initial choice is made, a second group of four actual items may be presented to allow him to select the item he wants.

For example, if the first choice is the picture of "sensory input," the next array may be a small vibrator, a surgical brush, chewable tubing, or a favorite smelling cologne. The child can then select the item he wants. As his picture recognition skills improve, you may be able to increase the number of pictures presented, or you may be able to present pictures instead of objects in the second phase of this exchange.

If the individual demonstrates more limited motoric skills, an eye-gaze system may be appropriate for initial choice making. The size of the choices (whether pictures, line drawings, or symbol objects) must be appropriate to the user's visual acuity. Once the size is established, the system can be introduced. Typically, an eye-gaze user is taught to look at all of the choices first in a systematic fashion (e.g., left to right, circular pattern). Then the user averts his eyes outside of the field (either closed, down, or to an area where there is no symbol) for a moment, and then returns his gaze to the desired object. As you can see, complex eye-gaze systems may require more cognitive attention and discrimination than other systems. This fact must be considered in selecting this method of choice making.

Other sensory systems (e.g., textures, auditory cues) may be paired with either picture exchange or eye gaze. For some students, colored or textured pictures (e.g., symbols outlined in puffy paint, picture made of a material like the item it represents) might be needed to allow them to differentiate symbols. For a student using eye gaze, an auditory cue might be needed to assist in identifying the pictures or categories presented. Generally, as the communicator hands the picture to the partner, the name of the item is stated (e.g., "Ball. You want the ball!") (Frost & Bondy 1994).

If an eye-gaze system is selected and the user is having difficulty locating or identifying the pictures presented on the eye-gaze board, a live voice scan may be added as a prompt to assist the user initially. Live voice scan involves naming the pictures or items available to the communicator with gestures as well as words and waiting for a response from the communicator. Live voice scanning can be particularly beneficial when the communicator's visual status is uncertain or his vision status changes throughout the day with fatigue. Once these auditory prompts are faded, the eye-gaze user can become an independent communicator by getting your attention through the systems available to him (e.g., vocalization, movement, slapping the desk, touching a switch) and then scanning the picture array to indicate the desired object. On the other hand, if these prompts cannot be faded, the individual may need a system with a combined input of pictures and auditory feedback to become an effective communicator.

Anticipation shelves

Anticipation shelves are much like visual schedules or daily planners that help the cognitively and communicatively challenged individual anticipate the next event. Symbols or pictures of daily activities are arranged on a board, shelf, box, or other support. As the activity is completed, the user (or caregiver) removes the task just completed and presents the next task. By using a visual representation, the communicator can see how many activities have been completed, how many are left, what the activities are, and in what order they will happen.

Anticipation shelves are particularly helpful for individuals who have difficulty with task maintenance or transitions. If the problem is task maintenance, the shelves are typically arranged with a desired and less desired task alternating throughout the day. If the current task is not a favorite, the individual can be encouraged to finish to get to a more enjoyable task. If the problem is transitions, pair the anticipation shelves with verbal and visual prompts (e.g., visual timer, marks on a paper) to encourage the user to anticipate the change in activity at the proper time with less struggle and resistance.

Case Studies

Michael

Michael is a child diagnosed with microcephaly, vision concerns, and no verbal speech. He is mobile only in a wheelchair propelled by others and relies on others for all personal care activities. He is able to move his hands, which are generally fisted, but repeatedly circles one fist around the other on the tray of his wheelchair. At his parents' request, he was served for several years in an inclusionary setting with his regular-age peers. He was well accepted but failed to develop skills expected on the IEP.

When Michael was in sixth grade, his parents agreed to a placement in a self-contained class for students with significant cognitive and motor concerns. He arrived in this classroom with a four-location device but failed to activate the device spontaneously to control his environment. A systematic series of prompts to use the augmentative communication device was attempted without success over a period of six months. The switch type and reinforcers were then systematically changed to encourage independent access and control of his environment. He continued to demonstrate significant difficulties and limited success with these changes. Michael had used a communication book in the past, but he always touched the picture located on the right side of the page.

When object symbols were introduced instead of pictures to associate with reinforcers (preferred and non-preferred), Michael began to reach to the object desired with no physical prompting required. He would discriminate between these symbols as there were some items he chose consistently and others he would avoid. It was also noted that Michael took items from both the left and right side of the display. After one year of intervention, Michael was using seven preferred objects for communication but still demonstrating no progress with picture systems and use of auditory feedback for communication.

Michael demonstrated many communication difficulties that interfered with his communication growth. He was extremely "prompt dependent" (always waiting for someone else to ask what he wanted or needed) as a result of being in an inclusive environment. He did not appear to see the value in controlling his environment (e.g., turning on lights or music) and would avoid making those activations to change his environments once he understood that his environment would change. Given his limited interest in external communication with others and his environment, Michael's progress was significantly limited.

Case Studies, continued

Daniel

Daniel is another young man with significant developmental disabilities. His functional concerns include very poor visual skills, limited motor skills, recurrent seizures, and significant upper respiratory difficulties. During a three-year period, Daniel experienced several surgeries for various problems and significant periods of non-school attendance due to illness. His home environment was supportive in spirit, but his family had difficulty arranging the physical environment of the home to accommodate the necessary interfaces and technology that Daniel required to participate in daily activities.

Daniel used object symbols to make his choices. Paired with live voice scanning (naming the items as they are touched), Daniel was able to develop to a choice of two objects representing two classes (activities and positions). Given his desire to accomplish these two choices, Daniel was motivated to participate. Eventually, he knew and understood nine objects and two groupings.

Because of growth, frequent surgeries, wheelchair adjustments, and other changes, the team struggled for 18 months before finding a consistent switch placement site that could be replicated with success for an extended period. Other switch sites would work for a period of one day to three weeks, and then circumstances or abilities would change due to his health, and growth and his ability to access the switch in that location would be lost.

When the consistent access site was found (switch placed on a platform above his right forearm so he activated the switch by raising his arm), a device with auditory scanning capabilities was introduced. Daniel understood the scanning features and quickly used the device appropriately to request changes in position and to select preferred activities.

Another communicative success for Daniel was his use of scripted speech on a multi-message switch. He enjoyed telling jokes and would use this switch to deliver messages to others in his school environment (e.g., office, cafeteria). Humor was definitely the window of opportunity for communication with Daniel.

Individual with Autism/PDD and Significant Behavioral Problems

Intervention Issues

1. Behavioral issues

Often students with autism/PDD exhibit significant behaviors that interfere with communication. These behaviors may be self-injurious or aggressive toward peers and others. Additionally, these individuals may demonstrate difficulties in transitioning from one activity to another, even if both are desired activities. Behavior difficulties may also be manifested as repetitive behaviors that focus the individual's attention inward toward self-stimulation rather than outward toward communicative opportunities in his environment.

- behavioral issues
- lack of verbal speech
- language abilities
- cognitive abilities
- motor skills

If the behaviors interfere with communication for the individual, it is important to address the behaviors simultaneously with the communication experiences. It is recommended that the communication team work closely with the behavioral management specialist to conduct and interpret the functional analysis of the behaviors and to develop communication targets to replace the identified negative behaviors. Teaching requesting and learning to follow a visual schedule may benefit the individual who acts out in an attempt to communicate his desires and exercise control over his actions.

2. Lack of verbal speech

Communication deficits and limited social skills are the primary diagnostic indicators of this population. Research indicates that 40-90 percent of children with autism or PDD do not have any verbal speech. Many others with this diagnosis demonstrate echolalia (repeating phrases they have heard in other contexts) and limited functional use of those phrases.

3. Language abilities

Even those students who learn to use words struggle to use their verbal language meaningfully in daily situations. One of the defining criteria for this population is a significant language delay identified by age three. Often these children not only lack words, but they lack the idea of functional communication to achieve an impact in their environment. They demonstrate significant delays in social signaling and other nonverbal language activities.

4. Cognitive abilities

The population of children with autism includes children with a wide range of intellectual abilities from highly gifted to significantly mentally impaired. Accurately measuring cognitive abilities in standardized forms is seldom achieved due to behavioral and communication challenges. Visual skills are often a strength for this population. Imitation skills (both verbal and motoric) are typically a weakness.

5. Motor skills

Motor skills, especially gross motor skills, are generally well developed. Hand skills are not typically impaired, although the lack of imitation skills often delays acquisition of independent feeding and dressing tasks.

Feeding issues may be compounded with oral sensory issues related to taste, touch, texture, and temperature of foods. Many times oral defensiveness (avoidance of things presented to the mouth/lips/cheeks) or oral-seeking behaviors (keeping items in the mouth for extended periods of time) are noted. There is evidence of difficulties in oral motor planning (apraxia) that may interfere with speech production.

- replacing negative behaviors with positive communications
- identifying learning strengths
- planned sabotage

Strategies

1. Replacing negative behaviors with positive communications

With the help of a behavioral intervention specialist, conduct a systematic evaluation of negative behaviors and determine possible rewards for the behaviors. Some behaviors may be responses to stimuli, but other behaviors may be initiations of communication. For those behaviors that appear to serve a communicative function, the strategy involves finding a replacement behavior that is widely understood by others that is a more powerful reinforcer than the current negative behavior.

Remember that there may be several reasons for a behavior. For example, an individual might bite his arm to indicate he is overstimulated and needs quiet time, but he may also have learned to bite his arm to draw an adult to him to accomplish a task (e.g., getting a desired item from a high shelf or cabinet).

The purpose of this analysis is to select communication targets that are powerful enough in their response to ensure that the individual will choose the new communication system over the previous negative behavior.

·96·

2. Identifying learning strengths (e.g., visual/motor/discrimination abilities) to implement appropriate technology

By determining the individual's sensory area of strength, you can develop the augmentative system most effectively understood by the user and others in his environment. If the individual does not appear to understand verbal cues and relies more on gestures, a visual system may be appropriate. If the user does not appear to understand verbal cues and does not look at visual stimuli, you may need to pair textures and physical prompting or guidance to initiate communication both receptively and expressively. Remember that true communication is a two-way endeavor that requires both receptive and expressive language abilities at some level of exchange.

3. Planned sabotage

Planned sabotage can be used most effectively as an implementation strategy after initial understanding of the augmented communication system is in place. Routines can be most helpful here. For example, if a child has learned to request a cookie using his augmented system, prepare a snack with a cookie on all of the other plates at the table except his, wait for him to ask for a cookie, and then "apologize" for forgetting to give him one when you served the others. Likewise, if the child has vocabulary that includes utensils, you could serve applesauce without a spoon. The key is to avoid a look of anticipation or asking "What do you need?" as you wait for the response, allowing the situation itself to prompt the initiation of the communication.

Target Skills

1. Initiation of communication

One important skill to teach this population is initiation of communication. If the individual does not acquire this skill, he will constantly be relying on his behaviors to communicate, or he will remain prompt dependent. Even early on in the communication process, it is important to foster independence for the individual as much as possible to help him achieve his potential.

- initiation of communication
- requesting
- refusing
- making choices
- waiting

Frost and Bondy (1994) outline specific strategies in their initial phases of Picture Exchange Communication (PECS) training that encourage initiation skills. Specifically, the communication partner holds a desired item and does not verbalize to the individual or ask questions with facial expression. Instead, the focus is on the desired object. The individual is taught a strategy to obtain the object that does not require waiting to be asked. The same system can be used with a voice-output system or other augmentative communication system developed for a communicator.

2. Requesting

If the person using augmentative communication is to learn to communicate, there must be some impetus for him to communicate. Generally getting things that a person likes or enjoys is motivating. In addition to things an individual wants, requesting can be requests for others to do things (e.g., read a book, color with me, turn on my video) that give the user more control over his environment.

3. Refusing

Effective communication also involves protesting or refusing activities, objects, food, and people in ways that are socially acceptable. These ways must be understood by others so that they can respond appropriately by ceasing (or not starting) the undesired activity or object. The ability to refuse gives the individual more control over his environment.

The importance of initiation of a refusal is seen when someone starts something or gives you something you don't want and didn't request. Much like "planned sabotage," this situation requires that the user indicate the refusal without a prompt from the communicative partner.

4. Making choices

Choosing between two items is perceived as a beginning skill, but actually, the idea of using your communication to get or refuse one item usually develops before the ability to choose between two items or options. Again, the reinforcement for making a choice must be adequate to entice the user into a communicative interaction. Choices can be as simple as choosing between two items or activities presented. Other options for motivating choices may include selecting which order the class lines up for recess, which table is dismissed first, or what music will be played during free time.

5. Waiting

Learning to wait and learning to postpone reinforcers for a period of time is a skill that is necessary for all individuals to function successfully in society. However, until a basic system of request and reinforcement is established, it is difficult to develop the skill of waiting. Logic tells us that first the communicator must trust that using his communication signal will allow him to receive a reinforcer before he can believe that he will receive it after a period of waiting. Once the ability to wait is understood and becomes part of the individual's repertoire, the skill can be used to promote group interaction and build independence from a dedicated caregiver.

Systems

1. Picture-exchange

The picture-exchange system developed by Frost and Bondy (1994) gives explicit instructions on how to train children with autism to use pictures to initiate communication. This system uses the principles of applied behavioral analysis coupled with the picture system and the child's known reinforcers to develop a system of pictures used to communicate with others. The specifics of this system are outlined in *Picture Exchange Communication System Training Manual* (Frost & Bondy 1994). Although this system was not designed to teach speech production, the authors found that many of the children using the system developed some spontaneous speech.

- picture-exchange
- voice-output
- scripted messages on successive keys

Picture systems can also be used as visual schedules and anticipation systems for individuals who understand visual messages more clearly than they can process auditory information. Understanding what is next from the picture schedule or task analysis in pictures can help an individual transition from one activity to another without a significant behavioral outburst.

2. Voice-output

The use of voice-output devices can be particularly successful for individuals with autism or PDD. Sometimes users benefit from hearing and pairing the picture with the word or phrase, and other times, they appear distracted or disturbed by the "talking pictures" and stop using the pictures to communicate on the device.

If you choose to use a voice-output device with a beginning communicator in this population, be prepared to move from fairly simple systems to highly complex ones as needs change. With a child with autism who has average to near average cognitive abilities, it is important to consider his ability to generate novel utterances. Also, his language development may not follow the path found in typical students learning language. The need for the language to differentiate between two choices may rely on the choices presented. Thus, the feature becomes important to achieve the desired outcome, as the language is expanded from "I want jelly beans" to "I want green jelly beans" when green and black jelly beans are both introduced.

3. Scripted messages on successive keys

Another strategy for beginning communicators takes advantage of learning how to select consecutive messages in a sequence with another person to gain a reinforcer. Using a skill the communicator already knows (e.g., left-to-right sequencing, alphabetic or numeric sequencing), a series of messages are recorded to complete a task or activity in the community, school, or workplace. The activity may be ordering at McDonald's, requesting supplies from the office/storeroom, or other simple tasks that require successive messages in a predictable sequence.

For example, along the bottom row of a 32-location voice-output device, there may be four keys with the numbers 1-4 printed on them. Since the user understands the sequencing of these numbers, he can learn to activate them one at a time to complete a sequenced message. The first square may say, "Mrs. Johnson sent me to get supplies." The second square may say, "She needs a box of small paper clips and a white legal pad." Message 3 might say, "That's all for now. Thanks for your help." Message 4 might say, "Good-bye. Have a great day!"

Sequencing of messages can also be used in reading books with repetitive lines so that the nonverbal child can participate with the group. The lines that are repetitive in the book can be programmed for participation (e.g., "This one is too big, This one is too small," and "This one is just right!"). This strategy not only promotes group interaction and socialization but also works on listening, attention, and literacy skills. For the individual using picture systems with or without voice output, the pictures should be paired with the written words, giving practice and power to using those symbols for communication and possibly promoting early literacy skills.

Case Study

Charles

Charles is a nine-year-old male who entered the public school system at the age of three. Following initial evaluation, educational eligibility was determined as Developmentally Delayed. Specific areas of concern to address in the school program were Charles' inability to follow directions, lack of verbal speech, high sensory thresholds for vestibular and proprioceptive inputs, aggressive behaviors, and limited interaction skills with others.

When Charles was in early childhood special education, a number of programs were introduced simultaneously to address his concerns. These interventions included the following:

- a systematic behavior management plan

- a sensory diet in the classroom and sensory integration therapy services

- a symbol exchange system for requesting

- an individual care aide to provide one-on-one instruction in discrete trial training

- a daily visual and tactile schedule to assist him in anticipating transitions

- music therapy

(continued on next page)

·100·

Case Study, continued

Charles' collaborative team met on a monthly basis to review areas of progress and to address areas of concern. As his aggressive behavior decreased and transitions became easier, Charles became more receptive to learning. Immediately following sensory integration therapy (and sometimes as conjoint therapy), the speech-language pathologist and occupational therapist began using pictures (rather than objects) to indicate the choices in the therapy setting. Eventually this picture system was moved to the classroom for daily communication, initially for receptive and expressive communications with Charles.

As Charles' picture recognition skills improved, he was provided a voice-output device with 32 locations (Alpha Talker) programmed with requests ("I want") and comments ("I like" and "I see"). These were programmed so that the object of the request or comment was on a separate key. Thus, to complete a phrase, Charles would activate button 1 ("I want") and then a second button ("cheeseballs").

Using this strategy, Charles quickly began to use the device independently. Although he did not transport his device with him around the classroom environment, he would go to the place in the classroom where his last activation occurred and use his device there to convey his message, even if others were not present to hear it.

As the team was addressing the concern of not transporting the device to the communication partner, Charles' behavior with the device began to change. He would no longer activate the "I want" button, but instead would put his finger on the button as if he were about to press it, and he would vocalize an approximation of "I want." He also demonstrated that behavior with the object words. Using this strategy, his team reintroduced the picture book at the table and topic or activity boards in particular settings and Charles' vocalizations increased. It appeared that once the vocalization was established, Charles no longer needed the voice output.

The team agreed that as a next step, new vocabulary would be introduced on the device to see if Charles could expand his verbalizations. This did occur and Charles was naming colors and numbers after a period of three to four weeks of consistently listening to the digitized speech recordings. It was noted that his inflections for the new words mirrored those produced on the AlphaTalker.

Charles is now being served in a classroom for students with autism. He has become an active user of his picture book, supplemented with his verbal output. Articulation is not at developmentally expected norms, but with the picture supports, Charles is able to convey his message to others in his environment and on field trips. He still uses the AlphaTalker to learn new words and also benefits from single-word productions in games on the computer. He no longer uses his voice-output device for communication but rather relies on his picture book and verbalizations. He learns new single-word productions from his voice-output device but does not imitate words presented to him in the classroom via live voice.

Charles continues to demonstrate growth in academic areas and is beginning to identify initial sounds in words. He uses a "Language Master" card system with the picture of the word and the printed word on the card to address his learning style. He still uses his AlphaTalker to add words to his vocabulary. It appears to the team that his best learning style involves the repetition of the word in the same way over a number of trials to imprint this into his lexicon, allowing him then to use this newly acquired word in a variety of situations, although his syntax remains weak.

Individual with Mild Cognitive Impairments and/or Mild Motor Involvement

Usually these children appear to be typically developing but are unable to communicate via verbal speech. These may be young children with apraxia, children with mild cerebral palsy, or ones with other diagnoses that cause the functioning of the oral mechanism to interfere with speech production.

- fitting in
- portability
- adequate vocabulary

Intervention Issues

1. Fitting in

Because this group is so cognitively aware, they experience the social consequences of being different more acutely than some other groups. Not only will the individual sometimes not want to take his device with him or use it in a new or unfamiliar setting, but sometimes the parents are also reticent, stating they don't want to draw attention to their child or they don't want him to appear "different."

Peer acceptance, family acceptance, and teacher/supervisor acceptance can all be issues with a person using an augmentative device. Without intervention, these challenges can lead to device abandonment in order to "fit in."

2. Portability

A second issue that must be addressed is the portability of the system and how that matches with the user. If the individual is ambulatory, can he have access to his device as he walks down the hall or does it need to be in his backpack for safekeeping? If it does need to be in the individual's backpack, how is he to communicate in the hallways? What is the backup system?

3. Adequate vocabulary

Providing adequate vocabulary in a combination of phrase-based utterances, as well as the ability to generate novel utterances, is essential for this population. Often these individuals will require phrase-based capabilities for typical social interactions but will generate novel messages in response to specific questions or circumstances. The ability to produce each of these will not develop without some specific instruction for finding vocabulary based on the system selected. Direct instruction will also be needed to learn to use the feature systems of the vocabulary program selected and to expand it to incorporate new features as needed. Finally, encouragement (and patience) from listening partners is essential to allow the individual to generate and produce his thought, even though it may sometimes be difficult or uncomfortable to listen to the silence as he generates his response.

Strategies

1. Scripting

For this population, scripting allows quick dialogue exchange to expedite routine conversations, bring attention to the speaker from others, and to increase the number of communicative responses possible within a day. This strategy in turn instills a greater sense of communicative competency and creates a desire for more communication throughout the day.

- scripting
- functional language activities
- computer programs (software) to target specific skill areas

2. Functional language activities

Designing functional ways to use language in the classroom and ensuring the vocabulary is available to do so is an effective way to increase the use and speed of a communicator's messages. If there is a powerful reason to communicate, the user is more likely to participate. Therefore, many support manuals for augmentative communication may include activities, boards, and overlays created for specific topics (e.g., "Go Fish" or "Uno" card games). By including not only requests and directives, but social comments as well (e.g., "You are so lucky! It's your turn! I'm out, so I win!"), you allow the user to communicate in a variety of situations during the activity.

For both school-aged users and working adults, it is important that vocabulary is available to meet a variety of tasks. The vocabulary selected should allow the user to convey messages with the accuracy and complexity needed for each situation. Sometimes specialized vocabulary may be required to meet the communicator's needs.

3. Computer programs (software) to target specific skill areas

The limited functional language user often requires additional support of software that can be connected to both his augmentative communication device and his computer. This allows the user to generate text from his communication bank stored with the augmentative communication device and later to print the information directly from his device to a printer without retyping the information on a different keyboard or computer. Sometimes he can also use this interface to access the Internet, allowing him to work and learn with tools commonly used by his peers. For example, a higher end or complex system will allow the user to connect directly with a printer.

device (with symbol system) $\longrightarrow$ printer $\longrightarrow$ paper copy with letters

Target Skills

- developing expressive language skills

- encouraging vocabulary development and syntax

- literacy (or pre-literacy skills)

- pragmatic skills

1. Developing expressive language skills

Developing skills in expressive language with augmentative communication is similar to developing expressive language skills in other arenas. SLPs understand that early communicators use one-word utterances, later move to two-word utterances, and then begin to formulate longer, more complex utterances with advanced morpheme use. The same developmental curve applies to users with relatively mild cognitive and motor impairments. If the individual is presently using no words to communicate, begin by teaching him the location of single word vocabulary to meet his wants and needs. Once those are established, encourage him to use two-word combinations to convey his thoughts and feelings.

2. Encouraging vocabulary development and syntax

The question that is often raised is "How high can you expect the language skills of a person who uses augmentative communication to develop?" Typically, individuals who effectively use their augmentative communication devices are able to generate messages nearly as complex as those they are able to understand. However, this language does not develop spontaneously, rather it is developed through creating situations and opportunities, carefully choreographing multiple scenarios in which a word or phrase can be used, and finally, through independent carryover to a less structured situation where the desired effect or result is achieved.

3. Literacy (or pre-literacy skills)

Most teachers have many questions about teaching reading to students who are nonverbal. It is often difficult to determine if sound/symbol associations are firmly established. Frequently the students will have trouble demonstrating what they know and what they can understand about reading and the reading process.

During the development, teaching, and assessment of literacy skills, it is important that the teacher, SLP, assistive technologist, and others involved on the educational team share ideas on assessment, teaching strategies, and functional application. Since each of these disciplines brings a different field of expertise, it is essential that they collaborate to meet the goals and objectives designed for this and other areas of academic achievement and demonstration of knowledge.

3. Pragmatic skills

An area important for users of augmentative communication that is often overlooked is the area of pragmatics (e.g., eye contact, turn taking, topic maintenance, change of topic strategies), the social use of language in context. Many times the nonverbal markers that typical speakers use in conversation are not picked up or used by the individual communicating with an augmentative communication device.

Some students will naturally develop eye contact to greet others and will indicate through gestures or vocalizations when they have something to communicate. It is also important for the communicator to indicate when he is changing topics. Sometimes a phrase can be programmed, such as "I want to tell you about something else." This comment allows the communicative partner to wait for the user, allowing him the opportunity to initiate topics as well as respond to communications. The device user can also use hand signals and gestures to indicate that he wants the communication partner to wait before changing the topic.

Systems

1. Voice-output communication aid (VOCA)

- voice-output communication aid (VOCA)
- travel books/topic boards
- assistive technology to interface with VOCAs

Given this population, the most common choice is a dedicated voice-output communication aid. The features of the system are determined through the evaluation process. Consideration should be given to the potential for growth of the individual's language system over the next few years so that the system will not be outgrown in the immediate future. Any new device requires a period of adaptation, and the less time spent on learning a new system, the more time that can be spent practicing and expanding language skills.

Another consideration is funding. Insurance companies and private funding agencies may have regulations governing how often devices (durable medical equipment) can be purchased, much as they do with wheelchairs. In this case, the device selected must be equipped with the technology the user will need for a reasonable period of time.

Often the ability to interface with a number of other technologies (e.g., printer, telephone, computer) will be important to meet the needs of this population. These interfaces will need to be considered as a feature match for the augmentative device selected. Consideration of multiple environments in which the device will be used (e.g., indoors, outdoors, different types of lighting at work and home) may give rise to consideration of one type of screen display over another. For example, a dynamic screen display device may require a cover or glare guard if the device is to be used outdoors.

The Source for AAC ·105·

2. Travel books/Topic boards

No single augmentative communication device can provide the total communication needs for any individual. Equipment can and will fail, either for a day or for a period of time. When travelling in a bus or van, it may not be safe to have a device mounted or even just sitting in front of the communicator as it could interfere with the vehicle's safety features. In short, planning for a backup system should occur at the same time that you are implementing the primary system. As changes are made on the primary system to address specific needs, be sure to consider whether those phrases, sentences, or features should be added to the backup system as well.

For some users, this backup can be in the form of a picture book or wordbook that they can use in case of equipment failure by their voice-output device. For others, backup may be a series of specific communication boards designed and used in specific situations or it may simply be a single-message switch or call button to indicate the need for assistance in accessing the device.

3. Assistive technology to interface with VOCAs

To promote independence and skill development in the school and working populations, there is often a need to interface dedicated voice-output communication devices with other assistive technology. By examining the environment and listening to the user, situations can be identified to promote these skills. The individual using augmentative communication may need to learn to use the telephone or take messages on the telephone. Learning to interface written assignments with the appropriate software that facilitates the transfer from the device to the printer may lead to development of job skills that the individual can use to gain meaningful employment.

Many sophisticated augmentative communication systems include infrared technology that allows the individual to operate a number of appliances in the environment, including the television, music systems, light switches, and others. This technology can increase the functional independence of the device user in his home and/or work environment.

Case Study

David

David is a 13-year-old eighth grader who attends school in an inclusive setting. During his preschool years, David demonstrated mild language delays. He was enrolled in a pre-kindergarten at-risk program and received speech-language therapy services. At the age of five, David suffered a traumatic brain injury when

(continued on next page)

·106·

Case Study, continued

he was struck by a car while riding his bike. Following the accident, David was in a coma for several months and remained in the hospital and in recovery at home for almost one year.

Upon his return to the public school setting, David received physical, occupational and speech-language therapy services both at school and in the hospital setting. His mother was primarily concerned with vocalizations as his speech modality. She was reticent at first about augmentative communication but eventually agreed to the evaluation. The team recommended a Liberator and one was purchased for him through his insurance.

During the next three to four years, David made minimal progress with his augmentative communication device. He was willing to use it at school with the speech-language pathologist (SLP) but did not use it in his inclusive classroom or in other speaking situations. His teachers were overwhelmed with his medical needs and relatively fragile physical state, and they accepted "yes" and "no" responses as adequate from David. He had an individual care aide with him all day at school. He was unable to use his hands to write but refused to attempt to type on a regular or adapted keyboard. He refused to learn the vocabulary for interactions and preferred to allow others to make decisions for him.

When David entered fourth grade, his teacher wanted to learn about the device and include it in classroom activities. As a strategy to involve David in classroom activities, the teacher, in conjunction with the SLP, made "cue cards" for basic concepts and words that would answer questions from stories presented in class. David began to participate, and his teacher continued to raise the bar of expectations for his participation in class. As the expectations rose, so did David's performance.

When David entered sixth grade, his software was changed from IEP+ to Unity on his Liberator. Given the length of time it had taken David to begin to use his device initially, this step was taken with great trepidation by David's team. David, however, responded to the challenge.

David is now in eighth grade. His brain injury has left him with limited verbal speech and significant language processing deficits. David is able to type and compose short paragraphs and essays on his device using the Unity software. His spelling skills are limited, but he accesses the word prediction program on his device when he is spelling and this has proved helpful for him. He no longer has an individual care aide and next year plans to enroll in the high school's assisted learning program to develop vocational skills for his future.

Adult with Acquired Speech Disabilities

Intervention Issues

• short-term vs. long-term use

• stages of grief

• identifying pre-morbid functioning

• determining prognosis

• soliciting input from the client

• investment/abilities of caregivers to provide support for the augmentative system

1. Short-term vs. long-term use

In the population of adults with acquired speech disabilities, many etiologies for the loss of speech come into play. Some patients may experience cerebrovascular accidents (CVA) or strokes; some may be diagnosed with deteriorating conditions; such as amyotrophic lateral sclerosis (ALS); some may be laryngectomees; and others may be victims of traumatic brain injuries (TBIs). One of the initial team decisions is to consider short-term vs. long-term augmentative and alternative communicative means.

Providing augmentative communication choices at bedside is imperative for all types of patients. The access and vocabulary choices may be limited at first for some users, but these can be built upon as skills develop. Other patients may need to use bedside options due to temporary conditions, such as a tracheostomy, where it is hoped that verbal speech will return as the primary mode of communication once the airway is safely functioning.

2. Stages of grief

Regardless of the nature of the speech disability, whether caused by traumatic brain injury, disease, stroke, or surgery, there is always a period of grief associated with the loss. Without the ability to communicate as in the past, the individual suddenly seems to be very different from the speaker we knew previously.

There can also be a great deal of uncertainty as to recovery of abilities, both speech and language abilities as well as the motor abilities that accompany an acquired speech disorder. Given the wide variance of recovery from brain injuries and the diverse course of progressive neurological diseases, it is important to begin implementation where the patient is currently functioning and to move forward with the available diagnostic and medical prognosis information.

With diagnoses of progressive disorders, such as Parkinson's, ALS, or others, there is always concern about the rate and type of progression that the disease will follow. There will be difficult topics to discuss including the extent and scope to be expected of the disease process. Attempting to develop a timeline for the progression of the disease and the rate and timing of skill loss is often difficult to predict.

It is important to consider family dynamics. Traditional family roles sometimes remain established, so if the patient has always been the decision maker, that pattern will continue. In other families, however, the decision maker role may shift to another family member, or it may be that no one picks up the role of decision maker and the family appears to be resistive or unwilling to follow through on appointments or activities requested by evaluation and treatment staff. Families deal with difficult situations in many different ways. If the family appears to be struggling, it is important to see that they are offered supportive counseling services, either through social workers, community agencies, or clergy of their choice. Without this type of support, families can become overwhelmed by the many changes and demands.

3. Identifying pre-morbid functioning

An important piece of understanding the type of communication system an individual may need is to understand the type and level of communicator he was before the loss of speech abilities. Knowing the person's level of education, reading abilities, interests, personality, and manner of speaking may help in choosing and programming vocabulary that the user feels comfortable using. Knowing whether or not the individual has typing and computer keyboard skills may allow him to use keyboard-based devices (if his hands are still working adequately) and allow him to program (type in) novel messages and phrases as he needs them rather than pre-storing more generic items.

4. Determining prognosis

An important factor in feature match assessment for some clients involves the prognosis for speech capacity as well as the prognosis for motor abilities. For example, a client with ALS may present with slurred speech but have relatively good fine and gross motor skills. Knowing that the progression of the disease greatly involves motor interference, the device selected may need to possess scanning capabilities. Although it may not be important at this time to determine the type of switch, the device itself must have the capability to scan as scanning may be the next step for the user as he continues to lose motor control abilities.

Perhaps a visual loss is part of the prognosis for the client. In this case, it is important to include an auditory scan as part of the feature match assessment. If you anticipate that the client will have progressive limitations in cognitive skills, the device may need to begin as a more complex device and be reprogrammed with a simpler set of vocabulary or even picture symbols as needed.

Medical professionals, understandably, are often reluctant or unwilling to provide a prognosis for a specific patient as the course of recovery or disease may have a broad spectrum of possibilities. In this case, you can ask the physician to state in general what patients with this diagnosis most often encounter to determine what programming capabilities should be included in the augmentative communication system being considered.

5. Soliciting input from the client

If capable, the individual who will be using the device should be allowed to provide input. He can state features he likes or dislikes about a particular device, as well as organization and location of vocabulary selections. If he wishes, his own particular phrases or common sayings could be programmed for him to personalize the device. Including names of family members and the names or nicknames he uses for those individuals may also increase the "user friendliness" of the device.

Make sure that the person using augmentative communication, especially if limited in his motor skills, has several ways to call for assistance wherever he is. Often devices will have a "siren" or "call" feature. When the individual is in another position, such as in bed or in the bathroom, he may be able to use a lower-tech device (e.g, wireless doorbell) to call for assistance.

6. Investment/Abilities of caregivers to provide support for the augmentative system

A great part of successful implementation for adults is ensuring adequate support following placement of the system. The support system for them does not always require trained professionals on an ongoing basis, as the adults who have lost speech production often retain their knowledge of language functions and structures.

Sometimes the adult can learn to program/adjust the device as needed for different environments (e.g., changing the screen display, adjusting the volume, adding vocabulary). Sometimes, a spouse may have the technical ability, the time, and the interest to program and adjust the communication device for the user. Other times, the most likely support person may be a child or grandchild who spends adequate time with the individual and can understand and demonstrate the technology for the older user. However, if there is no one in this position for the family, a number of "implementation sessions" should be scheduled over a period of six months. The frequency of visits will depend upon the nature of the disability, the rate of change, the complexity of the device, and other relevant factors. The purpose of the sessions are to discuss problems, learn more about the system, and become competent users of technical support available from the manufacturer, if needed. The overall goal is to ensure that the user has a support system that can address day-to-day needs and that the user knows when and who to call for assistance to keep him communicating to his fullest ability.

Strategies

1. Phrase-based vs. word-based

The same phrase-based versus word-based issues arise in adults as for other users. Given that phrase-based constructions are faster to access, they also limit the flexibility of the user to generate novel ideas and utterances. For most adult users with previously well-developed language skills, a combination system appears to work best.

- phrase-based vs. word-based
- pictures vs. words
- considerations for leisure/recreation
- promoting social skills
- developing a social support network/reason to use the device

Storing phrases that the individual uses frequently may reduce the cognitive load on social communication. Although slower, allowing access to vocabulary that allows word-based constructions gives the user a way to communicate specific ideas, needs, or emotions.

2. Pictures vs. words

Depending on the individual, the degree of impairment, and the cognitive functioning and processing skills, one feature match system that must be considered is whether the individual can communicate more effectively with a picture-based system, a word-based system, or a keyboard system. Several factors (e.g., location of brain injury, visual discrimination ability, word recognition, memory, spelling abilities, fine motor abilities) can affect the individual's ability to decode these symbols following a brain injury or disease.

3. Considerations for leisure/recreation

If an individual is able and wishes to participate in activities previously enjoyed, such as playing cards or going out to sporting or other community events, this participation should be encouraged and planned into the device. For example, if the user enjoys playing Pinochle, he will need vocabulary for bidding, reporting scores, and naming trump, as well as social comments about the game. Preplanning these activities not only helps the individual feel able to participate but also helps others around the person to recognize and respond to him as a real participant.

4. Promoting social skills

Sometimes it is important to provide feedback to the user about social skills. He needs to engage the communication partner in some fashion through eye gaze, gestures, or vocalization to convey the idea that he has a message to share. If the individual is generating a long message without word-by-word feedback, it may be helpful to the listener if the person using the device looks up occasionally and encouragingly while generating the message, and then looks at the partner with anticipation when the device speaks the message.

On some devices, a feedback feature of audible "beeps" lets the listener know that the sender is still generating a message. This beep system can take the place of the user trying to maintain eye contact at the same time he is generating his message, typically making it easier on both parties.

5. Developing a social support network/reason to use the device

As with any new skill, the more it is practiced, the easier and more natural it becomes. Additionally, with an augmentative communication device, the more we can find opportunities for the user to engage the device in situations to affect his environment and impact those around him by his words and wishes, the more powerful and desirable the tool is for the user. Therefore, it is important to develop a network of people in the environment for the user to communicate with. Generally, users rely on their primary caregivers to understand many signals and cues that they would not expect an unfamiliar communication partner to understand. Therefore, if a network of various communication partners surround the user for various activities, a wider variety of communication exchange opportunities arises.

- effective communication across environments

- appropriate social skills

- working in written text as well as verbal expression

- using the telephone/e-mail/other communication systems effectively with a communication system

- emergency call system

Target Skills

1. Effective communication across environments

It is important to target a variety of communication situations and ensure that the appropriate vocabulary is available for each. We have briefly discussed some social situations, but equally important are other routine situations where communication occurs. Appointments with physicians and specialists, social workers, therapists, and pharmacists are perhaps new activities for the user that now happen frequently. Ability to participate in worship services, shopping trips, dining out, and sporting events may also serve as appropriate and functional targets.

Some of these situations can be addressed by adding only a few words or phrases to an existing overlay or device. Other situations may have a vocabulary that is seldom used elsewhere and therefore requires that a separate set of phrases and words be stored in a special location for use at those times.

2. Appropriate social skills

Using a variety of greetings or replies is generally more important to adults than to children. They may have a "traditional" greeting they have used for years (e.g., "Howdy!") or special nicknames or phrases they say when greeting special children or grandchildren (e.g., "I see a beautiful, blue-eyed blonde coming my way!") that help the listener understand that this is still the same person—he just has a "different voice."

3. Working in written text as well as verbal expression

If the user is still interested in writing and composing written work or personal notes, consideration needs to be given to making adaptations to the computer or the device to provide him access. Some devices allow the user to store files, work on them on the device, and later print the finished product. Other devices can interface with the computer and allow the use of computer programs (e.g., word processing, data graphing, spreadsheets, games) through the augmented communication device to create documents on the computer in live time. Knowing these capabilities exist may be an important motivator for the user to increase his knowledge and skill on the device to accomplish personal goals.

4. Using the telephone/e-mail/other communication systems effectively with a communication system

A step beyond using the communication device for interfacing with a computer for documents is using the communication device to interface with other electronic systems such as e-mail, Internet searching (and surfing), using the telephone, and controlling electronic devices in the home (e.g., lights, TV, VCR). To the extent possible with the device selected, the user can access these features to "control" the physical environment and participate in a lifestyle more like he was accustomed to prior to losing his verbal speech abilities.

5. Emergency call system

Every user should have an effective way to call for assistance when needed. Several products that address these concerns are currently on the market. Some of these alerting systems are programmed into communication devices, but they do no good if no one is there to receive the call for help.

One other emergency backup system for the communication device user is a form of identification that is on the person at all times. This information should list the individual's name, physician, medical emergency information, and a contact person who should be called in case of emergency. This data could be in the form of an identification bracelet or some kind of identification card that the individual can show when needed. Many times the assumption is that the individual will never be alone, but in emergencies, the best laid plans can fail.

·113·

- high-end technology
- considerations for access

Systems

1. High-end technology

Most often, adult users who are trying to replace lost speech skills require a higher technology system that allows them access to a large vocabulary, a variety of constructions, and the ability to interface with print output modalities. Usually adults have the ability to read, so some word-based systems may be useful to them.

Because of the adult's knowledge of language skills (metalinguistic abilities), he can communicate with the assessment team about vocabulary storage techniques that make sense. The adult can explain his preference for dynamic or static display screens. He can share what features are important to him and what features he dislikes.

2. Considerations for access

Adult communicators need access to their devices in a variety of positions. The adult needs to be able to use his device in a favorite chair, at the dinner table, in the bedroom, in the car, and in other situations. This consideration may require different mounting arrangements for different situations, or it may be that the adult simply needs a single-message switch or call button to ask that someone give him access to his device when needed in those situations.

Case Studies

Julie

Julie is a 43-year-old female with a diagnosis of ALS (Lou Gehrig's disease). She initially presented with slurred speech and the complaint that speaking was becoming very effortful. With a medical background herself, she was aware that the course of her disease would most likely compromise her speech efforts long before she lost motor abilities in other areas.

While she was still able to converse, Julie explored a number of augmentative communication devices including a high-end dynamic screen device (Dynavox 2C), a complex static display device (DeltaTalker), and a portable keyboard with voice-output capabilities (LINK).

Julie selected the LINK as her device of choice based on several factors. She was a skilled touch typist and her fine motor skills in her hands were relatively unaffected. She liked the ability to generate novel messages as

(continued on next page)

Case Studies, continued

well as store vocabulary scripts (like the routine questions she asked her husband and children each morning before they left for work/school). She did not want to "learn a new language" as the static device required and she felt that she was able to access her messages quicker with the LINK than with the category-based system of the dynamic screen device.

Over the course of the next two years, Julie's motor skills continued to decline. Within six months she received a feeding tube for nutrition. By one year she required assistance for dressing and walking. Within 18 months she was in a wheelchair. She continued to maintain the ability to use her hands close to midline to type on the small keyboard provided to the LINK. Her final act before falling asleep for the last time was to type a message about her feelings to her husband.

Ron

Ron is a 45-year-old male who sustained traumatic injury to the left side of his neck in a knife fight. This injury created a left frontal infarct resulting in right hemiparesis. Ron also presents with severe apraxia and aphasia. Five years ago Ron began using a dynamic screen, voice-output, phrase-based communication system (DynaMyte) to communicate.

Ron currently uses writing, gestures, one- and two-word utterances, and a picture book to communicate his needs in addition to his Dynamyte, as this is his preference. Verbal speech is still attempted but remains fairly unintelligible and mostly consists of extremely familiar words. He continues to use a small communication notebook of words and drawings for communication in some settings.

Therapy goals for Ron have centered around social greetings using his DynaMyte, particularly to introduce himself. He has a part-time job in an animal shelter and meets new people regularly. Due to the limited intelligibility of his verbal speech, introductory phrases have been programmed onto his device to aid in the work setting. The motivation to use the greeting has greatly increased Ron's acceptance by others and has resulted in increased attempts on his part to use the Dynamyte. Goals for future use will be developed with the social factors in mind.

Conclusion

Each individual communicator with a system in place or a developing system will face a number of challenges—some expected and some unexpected. Illnesses, surgeries, change in equipment (e.g., wheelchairs, seats), and changes in educational, work, and home settings can all affect the use of the communication system. A system that is too complex may overwhelm the user and he may retreat from communication. Conversely, if an individual's device is not complex enough to meet his needs, he may not use it because he doesn't have the vocabulary he needs to address his issues.

One of the benefits of building a strong, ongoing support team is the ability to bring these problems, large or small, to the group. With collective knowledge and experience, the group is better equipped than the individual in finding strategies and solutions to address these issues.

Collaborative Implementation: Teaming for Success

6

Sharing the Vision

An ancient Chinese proverb states that "A journey of a thousand miles begins with a single step." Selecting and implementing an augmentative communication system for an individual is much like that journey. At the beginning, there is no guarantee that the trip will be smooth, that there will be no technological difficulties, or that the journey will have a successful conclusion.

If an individual is to be successful in her journey with augmentative communication, it is important that the team members work together. They must share a common vision of where the trip is headed if their work is to be effective. If any single team member is on a different path or steering in a different direction, he or she may encounter unnecessary roadblocks along the way.

The Evolution of Teaming

The team model for those working within special education has evolved since the passage of the Education of All Handicapped Children's Act (PL 94-142) in 1975. This law changed the way children were referred for special education and related services. Prior to the passage of this law, an individual could recommend special education or related services for a child, and the child would be assessed for those services. This is referred to as an *unidisciplinary approach*.

A *multidisciplinary approach* then evolved along with other client and family friendly approaches to services. Services could be delivered from a variety of therapists (e.g., occupational, physical, speech, and/or music), although they operated independently for both assessment and treatment purposes. An *interdisciplinary approach* then took teaming a step further, allowing the individual therapists to coordinate their efforts and provide services as a single team.

A *transdisciplinary approach* has further evolved in which professionals from various disciplines see the child together for assessment and some service delivery purposes. Ideally, family members are included in this team model. Advantages to this approach are that all professionals see the "same" child and are allowed to learn from the other disciplines and from family members.

Linder (1990) discusses an outcome of transdisciplinary teaming, based on work by Woodruff and McGonigel (1988). This concept is role release and has five different aspects. Each of these facets revolves around the sharing of information and providing the motivation to learn and support the roles of other disciplines represented on the team. The concept of role release is the beginning of working collaboratively on an effective AAC team for an individual in the educational or medical setting.

Role release as discussed by Linder (1990) includes the following:

- role extension
- role enrichment
- role expansion
- role exchange
- role support

Collaborative Teaming for Success

Working in a collaborative mode may be a new experience for many staff members. This model is based on the idea that it is unlikely that any one individual possesses all of the information, knowledge, and ability for every circumstance the child will face (Dettmer et al. 1999). This approach, much like the transdisciplinary team, strives to achieve a synergy from the team members rather than merely a compilation of skills and implementation of ideas.

In both the school and hospital system, one of the big concerns in forming a collaborative team is the amount of time that teaming will take. This may not be billable time for healthcare agencies, depending on the setting and requirements. With the need for cost management, often only billable activities can be provided for clients by health care providers in hospital settings. In the educational setting, it means finding a replacement for classroom duties (e.g., substitutes/teacher assistants) and adding one more meeting with additional duties that follow to an already busy daily schedule in the classroom.

IDEA 1997 reauthorization requires that parents be part of the teaming process and be involved in decisions regarding their children's education. Working around school, work, and home schedules can be a balancing act that appears impossible, but a rewarding and well-oiled collaborative team, once established, pays dividends far greater than the investment.

Defining and Sharing Roles

Several terms are used in teaming that deserve definition here. Often there are consultants who provide the initial evaluation for the child using AAC and then support the team in implementation in some capacity following the user's acquisition of the device. This does not mean that the consultant is "better" than the consultees (e.g., teachers, therapists, parents, or other caregivers), but rather that the consultant has a broader base of experience and specialized knowledge or expertise that may be helpful to the team. The consultant/consultee relationship is one geared toward solving problems together as they arise. Collaboration is "a way of working in which both power struggles and ineffectual politeness are regarded as detrimental to team goals" (Dettmer, p. 7). Collaboration, by definition, is "laboring together."

Effective collaboration relies on a basis of shared commitment and shared goals to address the issue(s) at hand. Therefore, there must be leadership to bring the group together, identify the issues, generate ideas and solutions, stay on task, and document results. If the team members are to equally share the load and the labor of collaboration, duties such as "recorder," "timekeeper," and "summarizer" must be divided and rotated among the team members. Encouraging different people to document the meetings expands each member's view of the group process by changing their focus, their perspective, and their appreciation of individual group member's talents and abilities.

Avoiding the domination of one member of the group is also a goal of collaboration. If we are to assume that members are equally invested partners in the progress of the child with AAC, no one member should always lead discussions or be relied on for the information needed. Also there should be no individual who always "gets her way" if the team is to mature and continue to benefit the AAC user.

Teams that are together for a period of time typically go through stages of development, some stages being more productive than others. Effectively managing conflict as well as harmony, avoiding "us vs. them" thinking, and ensuring that team responsibilities are equally shared will impact the ability of the team to meet its goal—effective use of the augmentative communication system. Several formal models of collaborative training are available for more work in this area, many of which can be found in literature on management and meetings in the business world. An example of a general form can be found on page 123.

Monitoring Progress

One of the essential roles of the collaborative team for the AAC user is to monitor progress. In the beginning stages of implementation, team meetings may be held frequently because there are many issues to discuss, plan, and prioritize. As the team becomes more comfortable and familiar with the augmentative communication device and process, they may choose to meet less often.

One tool that can be helpful to augmentative communication teams is some kind of benchmark or guideline checklist to ensure that all areas of language development are progressing. There are checklists specifically designed for augmentative communication, but any language development checklist can be adapted to track expressive and pragmatic language skills.

If the team has agreed on goals for communication for the child and have prioritized those goals, each member who sees the child should take data to report to the team at the scheduled meeting times. Identifying benchmarks or performance targets in measurable terms (e.g., "50 activations of the switch per day") will allow those collecting data to know where the skill is now, how much progress has been made from baseline measures, and when the skill will be considered "achieved."

Working on one or two priority goals (e.g., improving social greetings, topic maintenance) as a team across multiple environments provides the user with constant and consistent cueing and reinforcement. Looking at the data collected by the team can be useful in determining when and where the device is being used most (and least) effectively.

Identifying and Addressing Problems

The team data can also be used to identify and address problems that arise. If there are behavioral or social problems, the team should discuss a variety of strategies and agree on consistent ways to redirect, teach, cue, or model the proper behavior. Other times the problems may be mechanical. Physical changes may need to be made to the device, mounts, or classroom equipment (e.g., desks, computer stands) that interfere with the user's independent functioning.

Regardless of the problems and solutions identified, members of the team should leave collaborative meetings with an action plan that includes what action will be taken, when it will be done, who will do it, and (if needed) how the results will be communicated to the other team members.

Documentation of team meetings is valuable for transition periods where the user moves from one school or teacher to another, or for adults who change living environments or day treatment/care facilities. These notes can reflect any problems in implementation, strategies selected to address those problems, and the subsequent course of events.

Sharing the Ownership (Positive and Negative Sides)

For some teams, sharing ownership of the team is difficult. Teachers are typically used to being in charge of school teams. Depending on the setting in hospitals and long-term care facilities, physicians, nurses, and social workers are familiar with taking the ownership of problems and finding solutions independently. The concept of teaming involves learning to share and communicate with individuals from a variety of backgrounds, cultures, financial means, values, and educational levels.

If the team truly becomes a collaborative organization, the skills, knowledge, awareness, and participation of all members will be expanded and enriched. As skills and knowledge cross over from one team member to another, they are able to take the abilities and apply them to different environments. Additionally, for professional staff, they gain skills that will broaden their scope and understanding to avoid the same difficulties in implementing the next augmentative communication system that they encounter. For parents and primary caregivers, participation in a collaborative team provides an excellent theoretical and foundational knowledge they can use to share with the individual's caregivers in the future. Informed teams who have brainstormed, implemented, and evaluated methods, strategies, and equipment are better prepared to meet the next challenge for the individual that may arise.

If the team fails to collaborate and continues to work in a top-down structure with one individual leading and all of the remaining members following that lead, the leader gains the background and knowledge, but the other members only "carry out instructions." Without participating in understanding and developing the thinking process that contributes to solving implementation problems in augmentative communication, the other team members are less able to confront and address new difficulties as they arise. Additionally, the leader may "burn out" because she feels that she is the only one working on the team. Eventually the leader may abandon the meetings that allow interaction and revert to short written memos and directives to address implementation issues for the individual. Whatever happens, if the team is not invested and participating, the team loses. Often the biggest loser is the individual using the augmented system.

Circumstances may dictate that live collaboration meetings cannot be accomplished through traditional "sit down" formats. If the members are not available physically, perhaps the team can share their input via the Internet through emails or a "chat room" created for this purpose on the Internet. If the members are not available to participate even in this forum, the leader in charge of the group may need to enlist support and advice from various listserves and vendors who provide technical assistance to peers and customers. At times, the representative from the manufacturer of the device will make trainings available, either for a fee or for free, via both live seminars and courses on the Internet.

Whatever the strategy established to provide support to the implementation team, it should be strongly pursued and encouraged. Without this type of support, many individuals may face the issue of device abandonment that most often occurs not because the device is "wrong," but rather because the system has not been effectively implemented and supported.

Conclusion

Common sense dictates that the more an augmentative communication system is used, the more effective it will become for the user. The more the individual is supported across those environments, the less likely it is that the device will be seen as "impossible" or unnecessary in one or more situations. If there are physical locations where the primary augmentative system is difficult to use, secondary systems can be identified for use in those situations. Without the input of the team, however, these needed supplements can often be missed and augmentative system might be seen as a tool only for specific situations (e.g., school, doctor) creating a more likely scenario for device abandonment.

·121·

Teaming is work. It often appears much easier to just do it on your own rather than encouraging and devoting the time to a collaboration team for the individual. Personality conflicts will exist. There may be conflicts on big issues and even on little issues. In some teams, power struggles arise and may endanger the system implementation through sabotage.

So why risk it? In the long run, it is in the best interest of the individual when a variety of people with a milieu of perspectives and knowledge bases gather and share to create a single, solid base for beginning augmentative communication. With this foundation, the future for the communicator is one filled with promise and growth.

·122·

Team Meeting

Date: _____

Team Members Present

_____   _____

_____   _____

_____   _____

Team Members Absent

_____   _____

_____   _____

_____   _____

Group Roles Assigned

Facilitator: _____   Recorder: _____

Timekeeper: _____

Agenda   *Time Limit*

1. _____ _____

2. _____ _____

3 _____ _____

4. _____ _____

5 _____ _____

6 _____ _____

Actions   *Person(s) Responsible*   *Timeline*

1. _____   _____   _____

2. _____   _____   _____

3. _____   _____   _____

4. _____   _____   _____

Appendixes

Devices and Manufacturers

Ability Research, Inc.
P.O. Box 1721
Minnetonka, MN 55345-0721
(952) 939-0121
ability@skypoint.com

AbleNet
1081 Tenth Avenue, SE
Minneapolis, MN 55414-1312
(800) 322-0956
www.ablenetinc.com

Academic Communication Associates
4149 Avenida de la Plata, Dept. 317
P.O. Box 586249
Oceanside, CA 92058-6249
(760) 758-9593
http://www.acadcom.com

Access First, Inc.
P.O. Box 3990
Glen Allen, VA 23058-3990
(804) 935-6738
www.accessfirst.net

Adam Lab
33500 Van Born Road
Wayne, MI 48184-2497
(313) 467-1415

Adaptivation
2225 West 50th Street
Suite 100
Sioux Falls, SD 57105
(800) 7-ADAPTD
www.adaptivation.com

AMDi
Advanced Multimedia Devices, Inc.
31 Watermill Lane
Great Neck, NY 11021
(516) 466-2288
www.amdi.net

AlphaSmart
20380 Town Center Lane
Suite 270
Cupertino, CA 95014
(408) 252-9400
www.alphasmart.com

ASHA Products
American Speech-Language-Hearing
  Association
10801 Rockville Pike
Rockville, MD 20852-3279
(888) 498-6699
http://www.professional.asha.org

Assistive Technology, Inc.
7 Wells Avenue
Newton, MA 02459
(800) 793-9227
http://www.assistivetech.com

Attainment Company
P.O. Box 930160
Verona, WI 53593
(800) 327-4269
www.attainmentcompany.com

Aurora Systems Inc.
2647 Kingsway
Vancouver, BC V5R 5H4
  Canada
(800) 361-8255
http://www.djtech.com/Aurora

CIT Enterprises
P.O. Box 10028
Costa Mesa, CA 92627
(714) 751-6295

Communication Devices, Inc.
2433 Government Way, Suite A
Coeur d'Alene, ID 83814
(800) 604-5449

Communicative Medical, Inc.
Box 8241
Spokane, WA 99203-0241
(800) 944-6801
www.communicativemedical.com

Consultants for Communication Technology
508 Belleville Terrace
Pittsburgh, PA 15202
(412) 761-6062

Crestwood Communications Aids, Inc.
6625 North Sidney Place
Milwaukee, WI 53209
(414) 352-5678
www.communicationaids.com

Don Johnston Incorporated
1000 Rand Road, Bldg. 115
Box 639
Wauconda, IL 60084
(800) 999-4660
www.donjohnston.com

Dynavox Systems LLC
2100 Wharton Street, Suite 400
Pittsburgh, PA 15203-1942
(800) 344-1778
www.dynavoxsys.com

Electronic Speech Enhancement Inc.
12190 Natural Bridge Road
St. Louis, MO 63021
(800) 600-9819
(314) 731-1000
http://www.speechenhancer.com/ESEAdIn1.html

Enabling Devices
385 Warburton Avenue
Hastings-on-Hudson, NY 10706
(800) 832-8697
http://www.enablingdevices.com

Enkidu Research
247 Pine Hill Road
Spencerport, NY 14559
(800) 297-9570
www.enkidu.net

Frame Technologies
W681 Pearl Street
Oneida, WI 54155
(920) 869-2979
www.frame-tech.com

Franklin Electronic Publishers
One Franklin Plaza
Burlington, NJ 08016
(609) 386-2500
http://www.franklin.com

Great Talking Box Company
2211 B Fortune Drive
San Jose, CA 95131
(408) 456-0133
www.greattalkingbox.com

GUS Communications, Inc.
1006 Loantree Court
Bellingham, WA 98226
(306) 715-8580
www.gusinc.com

HyperActive Software
5226 Nokomis Parkway
Minneapolis, MN 55417
(612) 724-1596
www.hyperactivesw.com

Imaginart
307 Arizona Street
Bisbee, AZ 85603
(800) 828-1376
www.imaginartonline.com

Innocomp
Innovative Computer Applications
26210 Emery Road, Suite 302
Warrensville Heights, OH 44128
(800) 382-8622
www.sayitall.com

Intellitools
55 Leveroni Court, Suite 9
Novato, CA 94949
(800) 899-6687
www.intellitools.com

LC Technologies, Inc.
8455 Silver King Court
Fairfax, VA 22031
(800) 733-5284
www.lctinc.com

Luminaud, Inc.
8688 Tyler Boulevard
Mentor, OH 44060
(800) 255-3408
www.luminaud.com

Madentec
3022 Calgary Trail South
Edmonton, AB T61 6V4 Canada
(708) 450-8926
www.madentec.com

Mayer-Johnson, Inc.
P.O. Box 1579
Solana Beach, CA 92075
(800) 588-4548
www.mayer-johnson.com

MicroSystems Software
609 Worcester Road
Framingham, MA 01701
(508) 879-9000

Prentke Romich Company
1022 Heyl Road
Wooster, OH 44691
(800) 262-1984
www.prentrom.com

Pulse Data Humanware
6245 King Road
Loomis, CA 95650
(800) 722-3393
www.humanware.com

Remedia Publications
15887 North 76th Street, #120
Scottsdale, AZ 85260
(800) 826-4740
www.rempub.com

Saltillo Corporation
2143 TR112
Millersburg, OH 44654
(330) 674-6722
www.saltillo.com

Semantic Compaction Systems
1000 Killarney Drive
Pittsburgh, PA 15234
(412) 885-8541

Slater Software, Inc.
351 Badger Lane
Guffey, CO 80820-9106
(719) 479-2255
www.slatersoftware.com

Synergy
412 High Plain Street, #19
Walpole, MA 02081-4263
(508) 668-7424

TASH International, Inc.
11201 Greenwood Avenue
North Seattle, WA 98113
Ultra Voice
(800) 721-4848
www.ultravoice.com

Words +
40015 Sierra Highway
Building B-145
Palmdale, CA 93550
(800) 869-8521
www.words-plus.com

Zygo Corporation
P.O. Box 1008
Portland, OR 97207-1008
(800) 234-6008
www.zygo.com

Abilitations
One Sportime Way
Atlanta, GA 30340
(800) 850-8603
www.abilitations.com
Adaptive play and therapy materials
Seating, mobility, balance, mats, etc.

Academic Communication Associates, Inc.
P.O. Box 4279
Oceanside, CA 92052-4279
(760) 758-9593
www.acadcom.com
Software
Therapy and assessment materials

American Occupational Therapy Association
P.O. Box 64960
Baltimore, MD 21264-4960
(301) 652-2682
www.aota.org

Brookes Publishing Co., Inc.
P.O. Box 10624
Baltimore, MD 21285-0624
(800) 638-3775
www.pbrookes.com
Books with context applicable to AAC

Daedelus Technologies, Inc.
2491 Vauxhall Place
Richmond, BC V6V 1Z5 Canada
(604) 270-4605
www.daessy.com
Excellent source for custom mounting systems for
    devices on wheelchairs and other applications

Don Johnston Incorporated
26799 West Commerce Drive
Volo, IL 60073
(800) 999-4660
www.donjohnston.com
Wonderful resource for software and curriculum
    adaptations for students with disabilities
Highly useful catalog for all those who support
    individuals with disabilities in school settings

IEP Resources
P.O. Box 930160
504 Commerce Parkway
Verona, WI 53593-0160
(800) 651-0954
www.AttainmentCompany.com
Instructional materials

Imaginart
307 Arizona Street
Bisbee, AZ 85603
(800) 828-1376
www.imaginartonline.com
Picture sources, assessment materials

Mayer-Johnson
P.O. Box 1579
Solana Beach, CA 92075-7579
(800) 588-4548
www.mayer-johnson.com
Provides hardware, software, picture systems and
    support materials for implementation of
    augmentative communication systems for a
    variety of age and ability levels.

Sammons Preston
An AbilityOne Company
P.O. Box 5071
Bolingbrook, IL 60440-5071
(800) 323-5547
www.sammonspreston.com
An excellent source for aids and adaptations for
    individuals with disabilities in many areas
    including low vision, limited movement,
    activities of daily living, etc.

Thinking Publications
P.O. Box 163
Eau Claire, WI 54702-0163
(800) 225-4769
www.ThinkingPublications.com
Software and support materials for AAC users

http://www.assistivetech.com/prod-index.htm

Assistive Technology, Inc. provides information about a variety of AAC products and the populations for which they are intended. EvaluWare is of special interest and allows you to investigate the best computer access methods and ideal AAC setups for people with special needs.

http://www.remc11.k12.mi.us/lcisd/augment.htm

The Lewis Cass Intermediate School District (ISD) in Michigan provides answers to the following questions: "Who is a candidate for AAC? Why use AAC? What are some facts about AAC?" and "Where and when will AAC be used?"

http://www.professional.asha.org/resources/divs/div_12.cfm

ASHA's Web site for Special Interest Division 12, Augmentative and Alternative Communication. Provides information regarding the Division 12 mission and goal, professional and clinical issues, how to join, affiliate benefits, steering committee, and how to purchase back issues of the Division 12 newsletter.

http://www.pbrookes.com/aac/refs.htm

Paul H. Brookes Publishing Co. provides references for AAC books and articles.

http://www.aacproducts.org

The Communication Aid Manufacturers Association (CAMA) provides information on AAC workshops.

http://www.gusinc.com

Gus Communications, Inc. provides information about AAC products. You may select from evaluation CDROM, ALS/stroke information, speech/AAC software, computer access, environmental control (TV), wheelchair mounting, and portable computers. It also provides information regarding AAC products and Medicare.

http://www.aacinstitute.org

The AAC Institute, a not-for-profit organization, is a resource for people who rely on AAC, professionals and educators, researchers/developers/manufacturers, and those involved in funding. This site provides the goal of AAC, resources, and AAC Institute information.

http://www.augcominc.com

Augmentative Communication, Inc. provides latest information on hot topics in the field on AAC, news from the AAC community, AAC links, and links to online articles and presentations.

http://www.isaac-online.org

The International Society for Augmentative and Alternative Communication (ISAAC) provides information about ISAAC, an idea exchange, updates on events and conferences, resources, and allows for interactive news and views.

http://www.aac-rerc.com

The Rehabilitation Engineering Research Center on Communication Enhancement, which is funded by the National Institute on Disability and Rehabilitation Research (NIDRR), offers a mission statement, research activities, news and highlights, and AAC links.

The Source for AAC—Appendix C ·131·

http://www.aacintervention.com
   This Web site provides information on intervention products and topics such as where to begin with AAC, activity ideas, Boardmaker resources, potpourri resources and handouts, how to create literature-based communication boards, tips, tricks, smart sheets, and more!

http://www.frame-tech.com
   Frame Technologies offers information on products, price lists, and information about the company itself. Visual images of the products are demonstrated on the Web site.

http://www.temple.edu/inst_disabilities/acolug/
   This is the Augmentative Communication On-Line Users Group (ACOLUG) which is a LISTSERV created to exchange ideas, information and experiences on AAC by people from all over the world. It is a project of the Institute on Disabilities/University Affiliate Program (UAP) Temple University.

http://www.pacer.org
   The Parent Advocacy Coalition for Educational Rights (PACER) center's mission is to expand opportunities and enhance the quality of life for children and young adults with disabilities and their families, based on the concept of parents helping parents. This Web site supplies links for legislative information, workshops, how to help/donate, PACER projects, parent advocacy, transition issues, emotional/behavioral disorders, employment strategies, juvenile justice, health issues, and more!

http://www.csun.edu
   California State University at Northridge supplies links to conference proceedings and ideas for training, etc.

http://www.closingthegap.com
   Closing the Gap specializes in computer technology in special education and rehabilitation. Through their newspaper, annual conference, and Web site they provide practical up-to-date information on assistive technology products, procedures, and best practices.

http://www.isbe.net/assistive/aac_evaluation.htm
   The Illinois State Board of Education provides extensive information regarding assessments and the AAC team, when a child needs to use an AAC device as well as how to choose one. Information on issues such as the law, funding, and staff development are also offered.

http://www.aac.hhdev.psu.edu/Research.htm
   Penn State is a partner in the AAC-RERC (Augmentative and Alternative Communication-- Rehabilitation Engineering Research Center) which is dedicated to assisting individuals who use AAC by advancing and promoting AAC technologies and supporting the individuals that use, manufacture, and recommend them. This Web site provides information regarding their current projects.

http://www.aac.unl.edu/early.html
   The University of Nebraska, Lincoln provides information regarding early intervention and AAC (presentations, resources, etc.).

http://www.abilityhub.com/aac/index.htm
   AbilityHub provides product information on assistive technologies and AAC devices for both children and adults.

Every Move Counts
Sensory Response Assessment

Materials

large mirror
vibrator
dishpan of tepid water
hand puppet or small stuffed animal
pinwheel
two bottles of flavoring extract

edibles (sweet, sour, salty, bitter, spicy)
tambourine
music (tape recorder or music box)
an adaptive switch
three switch-activated reinforcers (sight, sound, and touch stimuli such as a moving toy, musical toy, and fan)

Directions

1. Do not interact with the individual while administering the assessment.

2. Position the individual in the way that allows the most opportunity for voluntary movement in that activity. (Several positioning options are illustrated on pages 65-73.) Some individuals must be positioned in such a way that you cannot see their faces clearly. In this case, position the large mirror so that you can see the individual's face in it.

3. Observe the individual's behavior for 15 seconds prior to presenting each new type of sensation. Note a key word describing the person's arousal state under Pretask Condition (ex: drowsy, alert, self-stimulatory, agitated).

4. Present each stimulus in the presentation-withdrawal manner recommended in the directions for that item.

5. Observe the client carefully during both conditions. Look for any event that appears to result from the presentation or cessation of that stimulus.

6. Mark the Scoring Grid.

Purposeful Responses

Purposeful responses include but *are not limited to* the following:

- Change in affect, mood, or facial expression
- Change in vocalization
- Change in oral-motor pattern
- Change in breathing pattern
- Shift in eye gaze toward adult or stimulus when activity is initiated or interrupted
- Visual search for stimulus or adult when stimulus is presented
- Motor attempt to stop or continue activity
- Motor movement of extremity

Name _____

Date _____

Examiner _____

1. **Vestibular**. Provide movement for 15 seconds, then pause for 5 seconds. Conduct 3 trial-pause intervals. Record response.

Pretask Condition _____		Scoring Grid		
		0	1	2
Rocking back and forth	Trial 1			
	Trial 2			
	Trial 3			
Swaying side to side	Trial 1			
	Trial 2			
	Trial 3			

Total Points _____

2. **Tactile**. Apply stimulus for 5 seconds, then remove for 5 seconds. Conduct 3 trial-pause intervals. Record response.

Pretask Condition _____		Scoring Grid		
		0	1	2
Vibrator (apply to muscle belly of forearm)	Trial 1			
	Trial 2			
	Trial 3			
Tepid water (immerse hand or foot)	Trial 1			
	Trial 2			
	Trial 3			

Total Points _____

3. **Visual**. Move stimulus through visual field quadrants (2-3 seconds per quadrant), then withdraw from sight for 5 seconds. Conduct 3 presentation-withdrawal intervals. Record response. Describe any differences between visual field quadrants under "Comments."

Pretask Condition _____		Scoring Grid		
		0	1	2
Puppet (wiggle side to side)	Trial 1			
	Trial 2			
	Trial 3			
Pinwheel (spin with hand, don't blow)	Trial 1			
	Trial 2			
	Trial 3			

Total Points _____

4. **Olfactory**. Pass scent directly under nose (not in contact with skin) for 3 seconds, then remove for 15 seconds. Conduct 3 presentation-withdrawal intervals per scent. Record response.

Pretask Condition _____		Scoring Grid		
		0	1	2
Extract #1	Trial 1			
	Trial 2			
	Trial 3			
Extract #2	Trial 1			
	Trial 2			
	Trial 3			

Total Points _____

5. **Gustatory**. Place a taste of food on the tongue and wait 15 seconds. Conduct 3 trials per food item.

Pretask Condition _____		Scoring Grid		
		0	1	2
Sweet	Trial 1			
	Trial 2			
	Trial 3			
Salty	Trial 1			
	Trial 2			
	Trial 3			
Sour	Trial 1			
	Trial 2			
	Trial 3			
Bitter	Trial 1			
	Trial 2			
	Trial 3			
Spicy	Trial 1			
	Trial 2			
	Trial 3			

Total Points _____

6. **Auditory**. Present sound from slightly above back of head at midline. It is important that the sound not be accompanied by movement within the visual field. Provide stimulus as described below. Conduct 3 trial-pause intervals. Record response.

Pretask Condition _____		Scoring Grid 0	1	2
Tambourine (2 sec. stimulus, 5 sec. pause)	Trial 1			
	Trial 2			
	Trial 3			
Music (record/tape; 10-sec. stimulus, 5-sec. pause)	Trial 1			
	Trial 2			
	Trial 3			

Total Points _____

7. **Causality**. Position switch so that any movement noted during the pretask observation will activate the switch. Assist in activating the switch for 10 seconds for each condition. Observe without assisting or interacting for 20 seconds. Score as follows:

0 = no observable response across conditions

1 = no change in frequency of identified response across conditions

2 = change in frequency of identified response across conditions

Pretask Condition _____		Scoring Grid 0	1	2
Disconnected switch	Trial			
Sight stimulus	Trial			
Sound stimulus	Trial			
Touch stimulus	Trial			

Total Points _____

Results

Enter the total points scored in each category.

Subscore Comparison

Modality	Vestibular	Tactile	Visual	Olfactory	Gustatory	Auditory	Causality
Subscore							

Physical Response Observation Grid

Indicate responses observed throughout the sensory assessment.

Levels	A. Absence of Gross Motor Movement			B. Head Movement		C. Extremity Movement				D. Mobility
				Side to Side	Up and Down	Upper		Lower		Describe
						Right	Left	Right	Left	
Check all that apply	Affect	Vocal	Eye Gaze							

Comments

Every Move Counts
Sensory Probe

Name _____   Modality _____

Date: Pretask: Activity:	0	1	2
Trial 1			
Trial 2			
Trial 3			
Trial 4			
Trial 5			

Score _____

Date: Pretask: Activity:	0	1	2
Trial 1			
Trial 2			
Trial 3			
Trial 4			
Trial 5			

Score _____

Date: Pretask: Activity:	0	1	2
Trial 1			
Trial 2			
Trial 3			
Trial 4			
Trial 5			

Score _____

Date: Pretask: Activity:	0	1	2
Trial 1			
Trial 2			
Trial 3			
Trial 4			
Trial 5			

Score _____

Date: Pretask: Activity:	0	1	2
Trial 1			
Trial 2			
Trial 3			
Trial 4			
Trial 5			

Score _____

Date: Pretask: Activity:	0	1	2
Trial 1			
Trial 2			
Trial 3			
Trial 4			
Trial 5			

Score _____

Date: Pretask: Activity:	0	1	2
Trial 1			
Trial 2			
Trial 3			
Trial 4			
Trial 5			

Score _____

Date: Pretask: Activity:	0	1	2
Trial 1			
Trial 2			
Trial 3			
Trial 4			
Trial 5			

Score _____

Date: Pretask: Activity:	0	1	2
Trial 1			
Trial 2			
Trial 3			
Trial 4			
Trial 5			

Score _____

Every Move Counts
Communication Assessment

Name _____   Date _____

This checklist may be completed based on the examiner's knowledge of the client or interview of the parent or primary caregiver. Circle the number that best describes each communicative behavior. Give examples of gestures, signs, symbols, or words in the blanks.

	Almost Always	Sometimes	Rarely	Never
Imperative				
1. Protests through:				
• Change in affect, vocalization, or motor patterns	8.0	5.3	2.6	0
• Gestures _____	13.5	12.0	10.5	0
• Signs, words, or symbols _____	18.0	16.5	15.0	0
2. Demonstrates discomfort or pain through:				
• Change in affect, vocalization, or motor patterns	8.0	5.3	2.6	0
• Gestures _____	13.5	12.0	10.5	0
• Signs, words, or symbols _____	18.0	16.5	15.0	0
3. Indicates hunger or thirst through:				
• Change in affect, vocalization, or motor patterns	8.0	5.3	2.6	0
• Gestures _____	13.5	12.0	10.5	0
• Signs, words, or symbols _____	18.0	16.5	15.0	0
• Spontaneous use of any of the above	6.0	4.0	2.0	0
4. Responds to removal of reinforcer through:				
• Change in affect, vocalization, or motor patterns	8.0	5.3	2.6	0
• Gestures _____	13.5	12.0	10.5	0
• Signs, words, or symbols _____	18.0	16.5	15.0	0
5. Indicates desire for more through:				
• Change in affect, vocalization, or motor patterns	8.0	5.3	2.6	0
• Gestures _____	13.5	12.0	10.5	0
• Signs, words, or symbols _____	18.0	16.5	15.0	0
• Spontaneous use of any of the above	6.0	4.0	2.0	0
6. Indicates wants and needs (other than those listed above) through:				
• Change in affect, vocalization, or motor patterns	8.0	5.3	2.6	0
• Gestures _____	13.5	12.0	10.5	0
• Signs, words, or symbols _____	18.0	16.5	15.0	0
• Spontaneous use of any of the above	6.0	4.0	2.0	0

Imperative Subscore _____

	Almost Always	Sometimes	Rarely	Never
Declarative				
7. Seeks attention through:				
• Change in affect, vocalization, or motor patterns	8.0	5.3	2.6	0
• Gestures _____	13.5	12.0	10.5	0
• Signs, words, or symbols _____	18.0	16.5	15.0	0

Declarative Subscore _____

Reply

8. Indicates "yes" and "no" through:

	Almost Always	Sometimes	Rarely	Never
• Change in affect, vocalization, or motor patterns	8.0	5.3	2.6	0
• Gestures _____	13.5	12.0	10.5	0
• Signs, words, or symbols _____	18.0	16.5	15.0	0
• Spontaneous use of any of the above	6.0	4.0	2.0	0

9. Responds to requests and directions:

	Almost Always	Sometimes	Rarely	Never
• When presented verbally only	11.0	9.0	7.0	0
• When presented verbally and accompanied by a sign or gesture	6.0	4.0	2.0	0
• With shaping or physical prompting	3.0	2.0	1.0	0
• Without repetition	6.0	4.0	2.0	0

Reply Subscore _____

Greeting

10. Responds to social interaction through:

	Almost Always	Sometimes	Rarely	Never
• Change in affect, vocalization, or motor patterns	8.0	5.3	2.6	0
• Gestures _____	13.5	12.0	10.5	0
• Signs, words, or symbols _____	18.0	16.5	15.0	0
• Spontaneous use of any of the above	6.0	4.0	2.0	0

Greeting Subscore _____

Attention

11. Demonstrates attention to people through:

	Almost Always	Sometimes	Rarely	Never
• Change in affect, vocalization, or motor patterns	8.0	5.3	2.6	0
• Gestures _____	13.5	12.0	10.5	0
• Signs, words, or symbols _____	18.0	16.5	15.0	0
• Spontaneous use of any of the above	6.0	4.0	2.0	0

12. Demonstrates attention to activity through:

	Almost Always	Sometimes	Rarely	Never
• Change in affect, vocalization, or motor patterns	8.0	5.3	2.6	0
• Gestures _____	13.5	12.0	10.5	0
• Signs, words, or symbols _____	18.0	16.5	15.0	0
• Spontaneous use of any of the above	6.0	4.0	2.0	0
• Attends to familiar activities	3.0	2.0	1.0	0
• Attends to novel activities	3.0	2.0	1.0	0

Attention Subscore _____

Total Score _____

Language Use

13. Please identify the sign, symbols, or words this person knows. Indicate what is required to elicit the communication.

I = imitative   P = prompted   S = spontaneous

_____ I P S		_____ I P S
_____ I P S		_____ I P S
_____ I P S		_____ I P S
_____ I P S		_____ I P S
_____ I P S		_____ I P S

Every Move Counts
Client Profile

1. Physical response mode (from Sensory Response Assessment) _____

   _____

   _____

   _____

2. Position selected _____

3. Pleasurable sensory stimuli _____

   _____

   _____

   _____

4. Selected activities _____

   _____

   _____

5. Targeted response(s) _____

   _____

   _____

6. Communication system

   _____ affect
   _____ vocal
   _____ motor
         _____ point/give/touch, look at
         _____ natural gesture
         _____ sign

7. Entry level (from Communicative and Physical Skills Matrix) _____

8. Comments _____

   _____

   _____

Fine Motor related to Computer (or Device) Access

1. **Current fine motor abilities:** Observe the student using paper and pencil, typewriter, computer, switch, etc. Look at the movements as well as the activities and situations. Does the student have voluntary, isolated, controlled movements using: (Check all that apply.)

   ❐ Left hand   ❐ Right hand   ❐ Eye(s)
   ❐ Left arm   ❐ Right arm   ❐ Head
   ❐ Left leg   ❐ Right leg   ❐ Mouth
   ❐ Left foot   ❐ Right foot   ❐ Tongue
   ❐ Finger(s)   ❐ Eyebrows   ❐ Other: _____

   Describe briefly the activities/situations observed: _____
   _____
   _____

2. **Range of motion:** Student has specific limitations to range: ❐ Yes ❐ No Describe the specific range in which the student has the most motor control: _____
   _____
   _____

3. **Abnormal reflexes and muscle tone:** Student has abnormal reflexes or abnormal muscle tone: ❐ Yes ❐ No Describe briefly any abnormal reflex patterns or patterns of low or high muscle tone which may interfere with the student's voluntary motor control. _____
   _____
   _____
   _____

4. **Accuracy:** Student has difficulty with accuracy: ❐ Yes ❐ No Describe how accurate, reliable and consistent the student is in performing a particular fine motor task: _____
   _____
   _____
   _____

5. **Fatigue:** Student fatigues easily: ❐ Yes ❐ No Describe how easily the student becomes fatigued:
   _____
   _____
   _____

Wisconsin Assistive Technology Initiative (2000)
Reprinted with permission.

Fine Motor related to Computer (or Device) Access, *continued*

6. **Assisted direct selection:** What type of assistance for direct selection has been tried?
(Check all that apply.)

❏ Keyguard
❏ Pointers, hand grips, splints etc.
❏ Other: _____

❏ Head pointer/stick, mouth/chin stick
❏ Light beam/laser

Describe which seemed to work the best and why: _____
_____
_____

7. **Size of grid student is able to access:**
What is the smallest square the student can accurately access: ❏ 1" ❏ 2" ❏ 3" ❏ 4"
What is the optimal size grid? Size of square: _____
Number of squares across: _____
Number of squares down: _____

8. **Scanning:** If student cannot direct select, does the student use scanning?
❏ No ❏ Yes, if yes: ❏ Step ❏ Automatic ❏ Inverse ❏ Other: _____
Preferred control site (body site): _____
Other possible control sites: _____
_____

9. **Type of switch:** The following switches have been tried: (Check all that apply.)
Then **circle the one or two** that seemed to work the best.

❏ Touch (jellybean)
❏ Joystick
❏ Arm slot
❏ Tread

❏ Light touch
❏ Lever
❏ Eye brow
❏ Other: _____

❏ Wobble
❏ Head switch
❏ Tongue

❏ Rocker
❏ Mercury (tilt)
❏ Sip/puff

Summary of student's abilities and concerns related to computer/device access:
_____
_____
_____

Wisconsin Assistive Technology Initiative (2000)
Reprinted with permission.

Communication

1. **Student's present means of communication:** (Check all that are used, then **circle** the primary method the student uses.)

- ☐ Changes in breathing patterns
- ☐ Eye-gaze/eye movement
- ☐ Gestures
- ☐ Sign language approximations

- ☐ Body position changes
- ☐ Facial expressions
- ☐ Pointing
- ☐ Sign language # signs _____
  # combinations _____
  # signs in a combination _____

- ☐ Vocalizations, list examples: _____
- ☐ Vowels, vowel combinations, list: _____
- ☐ Single words, list examples & approx. #: _____
  - ☐ Reliable no   ☐ Reliable yes
- ☐ 2-word utterances   ☐ 3-word utterances
- ☐ Semi intelligible speech, estimate % intelligible: _____
- ☐ Communication board: ☐ tangibles ☐ pictures ☐ combination pictures/words ☐ words
- ☐ Voice-output AC device (name of device): _____
- ☐ Intelligible speech   ☐ Writing
- ☐ Other: _____

2. **Who understands student's communication attempts:** (Check best descriptor.)

	Most of the time	Part of the time	Rarely	Not Applicable
Strangers	☐	☐	☐	☐
Teachers/therapists	☐	☐	☐	☐
Peers	☐	☐	☐	☐
Siblings	☐	☐	☐	☐
Parent/Guardian	☐	☐	☐	☐

3. **Current level of receptive language:**

Age approximation: _____

If formal tests used, name and scores: _____

_____

If formal testing not used, please give an approximate age or developmental level of functioning. Explain your rationale for this estimate. _____

_____

4. **Current level of expressive language:**

Age approximation: _____

If formal tests used, name and scores: _____

_____

If formal testing not used, please give an approximate age or developmental level of functioning. Explain your rationale for this estimate. _____

_____

Wisconsin Assistive Technology Initiative (2000)
Reprinted with permission.

5. Communication interaction skills:

Desires to communicate: ❐ Yes ❐ No

To indicate "yes" and "no," the student:
❐ Shakes head   ❐ Signs   ❐ Vocalizes   ❐ Gestures   ❐ Eye gazes
❐ Points to board   ❐ Uses word approximations   ❐ Does not respond consistently

Can a person unfamiliar with the student understand the response? ❐ Yes ❐ No

	Always	Frequently	Occasionally	Seldom	Never
Turns toward speaker	❐	❐	❐	❐	❐
Interacts with peers	❐	❐	❐	❐	❐
Aware of listener's attention	❐	❐	❐	❐	❐
Initiates interaction	❐	❐	❐	❐	❐
Asks questions	❐	❐	❐	❐	❐
Responds to communication interaction	❐	❐	❐	❐	❐
Requests clarification from communication partner	❐	❐	❐	❐	❐
Repairs communication breakdown	❐	❐	❐	❐	❐
Requires frequent verbal prompts	❐	❐	❐	❐	❐
Requires frequent physical prompts	❐	❐	❐	❐	❐

Describe techniques student uses for repair (e.g., keeps trying, changes message, points to first letter)

_____
_____
_____
_____

6. Child's needs related to devices/systems: (Check all that apply.)
❐ Child walks   ❐ Child uses wheelchair   ❐ Child can carry device under 2 pounds
❐ Child drops or throws things frequently   ❐ Child needs digitized (human) speech
❐ Child needs device w/large number of words or phrases
❐ Other: _____

Wisconsin Assistive Technology Initiative (2000)
Reprinted with permission.

7. **Pre-reading and reading skills related to communication:**
   ☐ Yes   ☐ No   Object/picture recognition
   ☐ Yes   ☐ No   Symbol recognition (tactile, Mayer-Johnson, Rebus, etc.)
   ☐ Yes   ☐ No   Auditory discrimination of sounds
   ☐ Yes   ☐ No   Auditory discrimination of words, phrases
   ☐ Yes   ☐ No   Selects initial letter of word
   ☐ Yes   ☐ No   Follows simple directions
   ☐ Yes   ☐ No   Sight word recognition
   ☐ Yes   ☐ No   Can put two symbols or words together to express an idea

8. **Visual abilities related to communication:** (Check all that apply.)
   ☐ Can maintain fixation on stationary object   ☐ Can look to right & left without moving head
   ☐ Can scan line of symbols left to right   ☐ Can scan matrix of symbols in a grid
   ☐ Visually recognizes people   ☐ Visually recognizes common objects
   ☐ Visually recognizes photographs   ☐ Visually recognizes symbols or pictures
   ☐ Needs additional space around symbol   ☐ Can visually shift horizontally
   ☐ Can visually shift vertically   ☐ Can recognize line drawings

   Is a specific type (brand) of symbols or pictures preferred? _____

   What size symbols or pictures are preferred? _____

   What line thickness of symbols are preferred? _____ inches

   Does student seem to do better with black on white, or white on black, or a specific color combination for figure/ground discrimination? _____

   Explain anything else you think is significant about the responses the student currently uses or his/her need for augmenting communication. (Use an additional page if necessary.):
   _____
   _____

Summary of student's abilities and concerns related to communication: _____
_____
_____
_____
_____

Wisconsin Assistive Technology Initiative (2000)
Reprinted with permission.

Assistive Technology Checklist

Writing

Mechanics of Writing
- ❑ Regular pencil/pen
- ❑ Pencil/pen with adaptive grip
- ❑ Adapted paper (e.g., raised line, highlighted lines)
- ❑ Slantboard
- ❑ Use of prewritten words/phrases
- ❑ Templates
- ❑ Portable word processor to keyboard instead of write
- ❑ Computer with word processing software
- ❑ Portable scanner with word processing software
- ❑ Voice recognition software to word process
- ❑ Other:

Computer Access
- ❑ Keyboard w/ accessibility options
- ❑ Word prediction, abbreviation/expansion to reduce keystrokes
- ❑ Keyguard
- ❑ Arm support (e.g., Ergo Rest)
- ❑ Track ball/track pad/ joystick w/ on-screen keyboard
- ❑ Alternate keyboard (e.g., IntelliKeys, Discover Board, TASH)
- ❑ Mouth stick/Head Master/Tracker w/ on-screen keyboard
- ❑ Switch with Morse code
- ❑ Switch with scanning
- ❑ Voice recognition software
- ❑ Other:

Composing Written Material
- ❑ Word cards/word book/word wall
- ❑ Pocket dictionary/thesaurus
- ❑ Writing templates
- ❑ Electronic/talking electronic dictionary/thesaurus/spell checker (e.g., Franklin Speaking Homework Wiz)
- ❑ Word processing w/ spell checker/grammar checker
- ❑ Talking word processing
- ❑ Abbreviation/expansion
- ❑ Word processing w/ writing support
- ❑ Multimedia software
- ❑ Voice recognition software
- ❑ Other:

Communication

- ❑ Communication board/book w/pictures/objects/letters/words
- ❑ Eye-gaze board/frame
- ❑ Simple voice-output device (e.g., BIGmack, Cheap Talk, Voice in a Box, MicroVoice,Talk. Picture Frame)
- ❑ Voice-output device w/ levels (e.g., 6 Level Voice in a Box, Macaw, Digivox)
- ❑ Voice-output device w/ icon sequencing (e.g., AlphaTalker II, Vanguard, Chatbox)
- ❑ Voice-output device w/ dynamic display (e.g., Dynavox, Speaking Dynamically w/ laptop computer/Freestyle)
- ❑ Device w/ speech synthesis for typing (e.g., Cannon Communicator, Link, Write:Out Loud w/ laptop)
- ❑ Other:

Reading, Studying, and Math

Reading
- ❑ Standard text
- ❑ Predictable books
- ❑ Changes in text size, spacing, color, background color
- ❑ Book adapted for page turning (e.g., page fluffers, 3-ring binder)
- ❑ Use of pictures/symbols with text (e.g., Picture It, Writing with Symbols 2000)
- ❑ Talking electronic device/software to pronounce challenging words (e.g., Franklin Speaking Homework Wiz, American Heritage Dictionary)
- ❑ Single word scanners (e.g., Seiko Reading Pen)
- ❑ Scanner w/ OCR and talking word processor
- ❑ Electronic books
- ❑ Other:

Learning/Studying
- ❑ Print or picture schedule
- ❑ Low tech aids to find materials (e.g., index tabs, color coded folders)
- ❑ Highlight text (e.g., markers, highlight tape, ruler)
- ❑ Recorded material (books on tape, taped lectures with number coded index)
- ❑ Voice-output reminders for assignments, steps of task, etc.
- ❑ Electronic organizers
- ❑ Pagers/electronic reminders
- ❑ Single word scanners
- ❑ Hand-held scanners
- ❑ Software for concept development/manipulation of objects (e.g., Blocks in Motion, Toy Store) - may use alternate input device (e.g., switch, touch window)
- ❑ Software for organization of ideas and studying (e.g., Inspiration, Claris Works Outline, PowerPoint)
- ❑ Palm computers
- ❑ Other:

Math
- ❑ Abacus/ Math Line
- ❑ Enlarged math worksheets
- ❑ Low tech alternatives for answering
- ❑ Math "Smart Chart"
- ❑ Money calculator and Coinulator
- ❑ Tactile/voice-output measuring devices
- ❑ Talking watches/clocks
- ❑ Calculator /calculator with print out
- ❑ Calculator with large keys and/or large display
- ❑ Talking calculator
- ❑ Calculator with special features (e.g., fraction translation)
- ❑ On-screen/scanning calculator
- ❑ Alternative keyboard (e.g., IntelliKeys)
- ❑ Software with cueing for math computation (may use adapted input methods)
- ❑ Software for manipulation of objects
- ❑ Voice recognition software
- ❑ Other:

Reed, P. & Walser, P. (2000), adapted from Lynch & Reed (1997), *Wisconsin Assistive Technology Initiative*

Reprinted with permission.

Assistive Technology Checklist

Recreation & Leisure

- ❒ Toys adapted with Velcro™, magnets, handles, etc.
- ❒ Toys adapted for single switch operation
- ❒ Adaptive sporting equipment (e.g., lighted or beeping ball)
- ❒ Universal cuff/strap to hold crayons, markers, etc.
- ❒ Modified utensils (e.g., rubber stamps, brushes)
- ❒ Ergo Rest or other arm support for drawing/painting
- ❒ Electronic aids to control TV, VCR, CD player, etc.
- ❒ Software to complete art activities
- ❒ Games on the computer
- ❒ Other computer software
- ❒ Other:

Activities of Daily Living (ADLs)

- ❒ Nonslip materials to hold things in place
- ❒ Universal cuff/strap to hold items in hand
- ❒ Color coded items for easier locating and identifying
- ❒ Adaptive eating utensils (e.g., foam handles, deep sides)
- ❒ Adaptive drinking devices (e.g., cup with cut out rim)
- ❒ Adaptive dressing equipment (e.g., button hook, elastic shoe laces, Velcro™ instead of buttons)
- ❒ Adaptive devices for hygiene (e.g., adapted toothbrushes, raised toilet seat)
- ❒ Adaptive bathing devices
- ❒ Adaptive equipment for cooking
- ❒ Other:

Mobility

- ❒ Walker
- ❒ Grab bars and rails
- ❒ Manual wheelchair including sports chair
- ❒ Powered mobility toy (e.g., Cooper Car, GoBot)
- ❒ Powered scooter or cart
- ❒ Powered wheelchair w/ joystick or other control
- ❒ Adapted vehicle for driving
- ❒ Other:

Control of the Environment

- ❒ Light switch extension
- ❒ Use of interface and switch to activate battery operated devices
- ❒ Use of interface and switch to turn on electrical appliances (e.g., radio, fan, blender)
- ❒ Radio/ultra sound to remotely control appliances
- ❒ Use of electronic aid to daily living to control environment in connection with an augmentative communication device
- ❒ Other:

Positioning & Seating

- ❒ Non-slip surface on chair to prevent slipping (e.g., Dycem)
- ❒ Bolster, rolled towel, blocks for feet
- ❒ Adapted/alternate chair, sidelyer, stander
- ❒ Custom fitted wheelchair or insert
- ❒ Other:

Vision

- ❒ Eye glasses
- ❒ Magnifier
- ❒ Large print books
- ❒ CCTV (closed circuit television)
- ❒ Screen magnifier (mounted over screen)
- ❒ Screen magnification software
- ❒ Screen color contrast
- ❒ Screen reader, text reader
- ❒ Braille translation software
- ❒ Braille printer
- ❒ Enlarged or Braille/tactile labels for keyboard
- ❒ Alternate keyboard with enlarged keys
- ❒ Braille keyboard and note taker
- ❒ Other:

Hearing

- ❒ Pen and paper
- ❒ Computer/portable word processor
- ❒ TDD/TTY for phone access with or without relay
- ❒ Signaling device (e.g., flashing light or vibrating pager)
- ❒ Closed Captioning
- ❒ Real Time captioning
- ❒ Computer aided note taking
- ❒ Screen flash for alert signals on computer
- ❒ Phone amplifier
- ❒ Personal amplification system/Hearing aid
- ❒ FM or Loop system
- ❒ Infrared system
- ❒ Other:

Comments:

_____

_____

_____

_____

_____

_____

_____

_____

Reed, P. & Walser, P. (2000), adapted from Lynch & Reed (1997), *Wisconsin Assistive Technology Initiative*

Reprinted with permission.

Wisconsin Assistive Technology Initiative
Assistive Technology Planning Guide

PROBLEM IDENTIFICATION		
Student's Abilities/Difficulties (Related to Tasks)	**Environmental Considerations**	**Tasks:** What does the student need to be able to do?
Writing/Use of Hands: Communication: Reading Cognition: Mobility: Vision: Hearing: Behavior: Other:	e.g., classroom, playground, lunchroom, home; IBM compatible computer in room available for all children, voice-output device available in classroom, etc.; students sit on floor for calendar, desks arranged in groups of four; chalkboard at end of long room	e.g., produce legible written material, product audible speech, read text, complete math problems, participate in rec/leisure, move independently in the school environment ┌──────────────────────┐ Task(s) identified for Solution Generation └──────────────────────┘

Solution—Generation	Solution—Selection	Implementation Plan

Brainstorming Only - no decision
 	
Resources:
   AT Checklist
   Technology Toolbox
   CTG Resource Directory
   Co-Net CD
   AAC Feature Match/Needs First
     your AT Consultant
	Discuss & Select best ideas from brainstorming	AT services needed. AT trial: how long, when, person(s) responsible
		
		┌──────────────────────┐
		Follow-up Plan
		└──────────────────────┘
		
		Who & When—Set specific date now.

Lynch & Reed (1997), Incorporation from SETT framework (Zabala, 1994)

Note: It is not intended that you write on this page. Each topic should be written where everyone can see them (i.e., on a flip chart, board or overhead projector). Information should then be copied on paper for file or future reference.

Reprinted with permission.

Wisconsin Assistive Technology Initiative
Assistive Technology Consideration Guide

Student: _____   School: _____

1. What task is it that we want this student to do, that s/he is unable to do at a level that reflects his/her skills/abilities (writing, reading, communicating, seeing, hearing)? Document by checking each relevant task below. Please leave blank any tasks which are not relevant to the student's IEP.
2. Is the student currently able to complete tasks with special strategies or accommodations? If yes, describe in column A for each checked task.
3. Is there available assistive technology (either devices, tools, hardware, or software) that could be used to address this task? If yes, describe in column B. If any assistive technology tools are currently being used (or were tried in the past), describe in column B. (If none are known, review WATI's AT Checklist.)
4. Would the use of assistive technology help the student perform this skill more easily or efficiently, in the least restrictive environment, or perform successfully with less personal assistance? If yes, complete column C.

Tasks:	A. If currently completes task with special strategies/accommodations, describe.	B. If currently completes task with assistive technology tools, describe.	C. Describe new or additional assistive technology to be tried.
☐ Mechanics of Writing			
☐ Computer Access			
☐ Composing Written Material			
☐ Communication			
☐ Reading			
☐ Learning/Studying			

Tasks:	A. If currently completes task with special strategies/accommodations, describe.	B. If currently completes task with assistive technology tools, describe.	C. Describe new or additional assistive technology to be tried.
❑ Math			
❑ Recreation & Leisure			
❑ Activities of Daily Living (ADLs)			
❑ Mobility			
❑ Environmental Control			
❑ Positioning & Seating			
❑ Vision			
❑ Hearing			

5. Are there assistive technology services (more specific evaluation of need for assistive technology, adapting or modifying the assistive technology, technical assistance on its operation or use, or training of student, staff, or family) that this student needs? If yes, describe what will be provided, the initiation and duration: _____

Persons Present: _____   Date: _____

Wisconsin Assistive Technology Initiative
Assistive Technology Assessment Procedure Guide
for School Districts/Birth-3 Programs

School District: _____ School: _____

Student: _____ Grade: _____

Team Members: _____

Date Completed:

Before the Meeting:

Step 1: **Team Members Gather Information.** Review existing information regarding child's abilities, difficulties, environment, and tasks. If there is missing information, you will need to gather the information by completing formal tests (e.g., Bruininks-Oseretsky, Peabody), completing informal tests, and/or observing the child in various settings. The WATI Student Information Guide and Environmental Observation Guide are used to assist with gathering information.

Stem 2: **Schedule Meeting.** Schedule the meeting with team. Team includes: Parents, student (if approp.), service providers (e.g., Spec. Ed. Teach., Gen. Ed. Teach., SLP, OT, PT, Admin.), and others.

At the Meeting:

Step 3: **Team Completes Problem Identification Portion of AT Planning Guide.** Choose someone to write all topics where everyone participating can see them. The emphasis in Problem Identification is identifying tasks the child needs to be able to do and the relationship of the child's abilities/difficulties and environment to the child's performance of the tasks.

Note: Team should move quickly through listing "Student's Abilities/Difficulties related to tasks" (5-10 min). Team should move quickly through "Environmental Considerations" (5-10 min.), listing key aspects of the the environment in which the child functions and the child's location and positioning within the environment. **Identifying the Tasks the child needs to be able to do is important because the Team cannot generate AT Solutions until the Tasks have been identified.**

Step 4: **Choose Tasks for Solution Generation.** Identify 1 (or possibly 2) critical tasks for which the team will generate solutions.

Step 5: **Solution Generation**. Brainstorm all possible solutions.

Note: The specificity of the solutions will vary depending on the knowledge and experience of the team members; some teams may generate names of specific devices with features that will meet the child's needs, other teams may simply talk about features that are important (e.g., "needs voice output," "needs to be portable," "needs few (or many) messages," "needs input method other than hands,"). Teams may want to use specific resources to assist with Solution Generation. These resources include: the AT Checklist, the ASNAT manual, the Tool Box in Computer Resources for People with Disabilities, AAC match or Needs First software, Trace Resource Book, Closing the Gap Directory, and/or WATI consultant.

Step 6: **Solution Selection.** Discuss the solutions listed, thinking about which are most effective for the student. It may help to identify solutions which can be implemented 1) immediately, 2) in the next few months, and 3) in the future. At this point list names of specific devices, hardware, software, etc. If the team does not know the names of devices, etc., use resources noted in Step 5.

Step 7: **Implementation Plan.** Develop Implementation Plan (including trials with equipment)—being sure to assign names and dates and Follow-Up Plan.

▲**Reminder:** Steps 3-7 occur in a meeting with all topics written where all participants can see them because decision making is a process which involves service providers who work with a child in his/her customary environment and the child's parents. Use a flip chart, board or overhead during the meeting and ensure that someone transfers the information to paper for the child's file or future reference.

After the Meeting:

Step 8: **Implement**

Step 9: **Follow Up on Planned Date**

Lynch & Reed (1997), Wisconsin Assistive Technology Initiative   Rev. 9/98

Reprinted with permission.

Illinois Department of Public Aid
Augmentative Communication Systems
Client Assessment Report

Date: _____

Client: _____

Client Case Number: _____

Assessment team members:

Speech-language pathologist: _____

Primary care physician: _____

Parent(s) or primary care giver: _____

Other medical professionals: _____

Client demographic/biographic summary:

Diagnosis and reason for referral:

_____

_____

_____

_____

Age: _____

Approximate physical size (height and weight):

_____

Living arrangement (e.g., with family and size and composition, in a nursing or group facility):

_____

Primary occupation(s) (e.g., school and grade level, employment and type, workshop or day treatment, stays at home):

_____

List of other supportive resource individuals, if any (e.g., family members, friends, aid at school or work, in-home worker, facility staff):

_____

DPA 3641 (R-4-2000)   IL478-2337

Reprinted with permission.

Inventory of skill levels sensory function and use of assistive devices, if any, in the following areas:

Vision:

_____

_____

Hearing:

_____

_____

Ambulation mode(s), including appropriateness of seating/positioning, if applicable:

_____

_____

Functional gross and fine motor skills in head/neck, trunk, and all four extremities:

_____

_____

Cognition and learning potential, to include:

• object permanence (ability to remember objects and realize they exist when they are not seen):

_____

_____

• cause and effect (ability to associate certain behaviors or event with actions that will follow):

_____

_____

• means end (ability to anticipate events independent of those currently in progress):

_____

_____

• cognitive level (to include any available, recent standard or observational measurements of mental and developmental ages, and demonstrated consistent ability to attend, match, categorize, and sequence):

_____

_____

_____

_____

<u>Inventory of the present and anticipated future communication levels for each of the following:</u>

Type of expressive communication method/mode(s) used:

_____

_____

_____

Functional level of oral, written and gestural expressive language capabilities, including oral motor speech status, and the communication functions of requesting, protesting, labeling and sharing information:

_____

_____

_____

_____

_____

_____

_____

Communicative interest:

_____

_____

_____

Identification of a reliable and consistent motor response which can be used independently to communicate:

_____

_____

<u>Assessment of present and future communication needs, including the types of communication needed, with whom, and in what environments</u> (e.g., to enhance conversation, and/or to write and signal emergency, basic care and related medical needs):

_____

_____

_____

_____

_____

Features needed in client communication system, as applicable:

Type and number of messages, vocabulary size, coding system, symbol sets, message retrieval:

_____

_____

_____

_____

_____

Size, layout, system memory, optical indicators, auditory prompts, rate enhancement, programmability, computer compatibility:

_____

_____

_____

_____

_____

Type of input method (e.g., switches, mouth stick, head pointer, alternative keyboard, and direct selection, scanning, encoding):

_____

Type of output (e.g., speech, print, LCD, braille):

_____

Mounting and portability:

_____

Extent of training required to use the system and availability of training and technical assistance for its use:

_____

_____

Availability of customer service by manufacturer or supplier:

_____

_____

Availability of trial rental period and statement regarding whether rental fees can be applied towards purchase price:

_____

_____

Other considerations:

_____

_____

_____

<u>Summary of intervention options, to include:</u>

- <u>Description of the systems tried by client during or prior to the assessment and success in terms of actual ability, motivation, independence. and improvement in communication effectiveness:</u>

_____

_____

_____

_____

_____

_____

_____

_____

- <u>The advantages, disadvantages, cost, and availability of training/customer service, for the two or three most appropriate communication systems for the client as determined through the assessment, specifying available features and client needs for each:</u>

_____

_____

_____

_____

_____

_____

_____

_____

- Documentation of client trial and success, including ability, motivation, independence, and improvement in communication effectiveness, in using one or more recommended communication systems, which may be accomplished prior to or during the assessment, or the rental cost for which may be requested through the prior approval process following the assessment:

_____

_____

_____

_____

_____

_____

- Final recommendation of which system is most appropriate to meet the client's medical needs and why, to include documentation of a vendor's price quote, a copy of the warranty, the availability of maintenance, the shipping location, and a recommendation of at least one other system which would meet the client's medical needs. (Department approval will be based on the most cost effective system that meets the individual's medical needs.)

_____

_____

_____

_____

(Attach additional pages if necessary)

Required Attachments:

1. Prescription and Certification of Medical Necessity (including medical history information)
2. Individual Treatment and Implementation Plan
3. Literature on Recommended Equipment

Signature of Preparer: _____

Address: _____

_____

_____

Phone: _____

Illinois Department of Public Aid
Augmentative Communication Systems
Client Assessment Report

Date: _April 5, 2002_

Client: _Leslie Montgomery_

Client Case Number: _XX-XXX-XX-XXXXXX_   Client Case Number: _XXX-XXX-XXX_

Assessment team members:

Speech-language pathologist:	Daisy Page, CCC-SLP
Primary care physician:	Dr. Amos Farrigno
Parent(s) or primary care giver:	Michelle Montgomery
Other medical professionals:	Shriner's Clinic, St. Louis
Assistive technologist:	Glenda Hand, MPH, OTR/L
Augmentative communication specialist:	Ellen Talker, M.S., CCC-SLP

Client demographic/biographic summary:

Diagnosis and reason for referral:

Leslie has a diagnosis of cerebral palsy. Her speech is limited to vocal sounds and limited word approximations. She has previously owned a device for generating speech but that device (purchased sometime prior to 1993) is broken and cannot be repaired. This referral is to assist the local assessment team to determine the speech generating device that could be most helpful to Leslie to meet her functional communication needs.

Age: 16

Approximate physical size (height and weight):

5 ft, 5 inches; 135 lbs.

Living arrangement (e.g., with family and size and composition, in a nursing or group facility):

Lives at home with her mother and twin sister

Primary occupation(s) (e.g., school and grade level, employment and type, workshop or day treatment, stays at home):

Leslie attends Lincoln High School and participates in the Assisted Living Program there.

List of other supportive resource individuals, if any (e.g., family members, friends, aid at school or work, in-home worker, facility staff):

School staff is extremely supportive of Leslie and have worked with her to use the communication systems provided by the augmentative communication team to address her needs during school and community activities. Support staff there include her classroom teacher, speech-language pathologist, physical and occupational therapists, and employment coaches. In the home environment, Leslie relies on her mother and her sibling for personal care needs she cannot accomplish independently.

<u>Inventory of skill levels sensory function and use of assistive devices, if any, in the following areas:</u>

Vision:

> Leslie's vision is adequate. There are no concerns in this area.

Hearing:

> Hearing screenings at school have been passed. There are no concerns in this area.

Ambulation mode(s), including appropriateness of seating/positioning, if applicable:

> Leslie is able to walk without assistance, although her gait is uneven and stability is challenging on uneven surfaces.
> She has limited ability to carry heavy items while walking due to balance problems.

Functional gross and fine motor skills in head/neck, trunk, and all four extremities:

> Leslie is able to functionally use her legs for ambulation. Leslie's right upper extremity is generally used only as an assist for functional tasks and she wears a resting hand splint on this hand. Her left hand is used for all functional fine motor tasks including writing, self-care, and button selection of the communication device. She demonstrates normal range of motion, strength, and targeting abilities of this extremity. She requires no adaptations in its use. She cannot transfer items from hand to hand.

Cognition and learning potential, to include:

- <u>object permanence</u> (ability to remember objects and realize they exist when they are not seen):

> present

- <u>cause and effect</u> (ability to associate certain behaviors or event with actions that will follow):

> present

- <u>means end</u> (ability to anticipate events independent of those currently in progress):

> present

- <u>cognitive level</u> (to include any available, recent standard or observational measurements of mental and developmental ages, and demonstrated consistent ability to attend, match, categorize, and sequence):

> Measures of cognitive abilities over time have demonstrated Leslie's abilities are in the mildly mentally impaired range. Functionally she is able to read some basic sight words. Her spelling skills are weak. She recently has demonstrated interest in learning to decode words phonetically. She can do simple math and uses some low-tech adaptations to make handwriting more manageable. Given a model, she is able to copy words or simple designs presented to her. She is able to sort by categories and sequence activities presented in picture form.

<u>Inventory of the present and anticipated future communication levels for each of the following:</u>

Type of expressive communication method/mode(s) used:

> Leslie interacts with others primarily through gestures, facial expressions, and vocalizations. She greets her peers with a wave and vocalization. When she is reluctant to participate, she communicates by lowering her eyes and turning away. Leslie maintains appropriate eye contact during communication exchanges. She initiates conversations with others and will continue those exchanges by use of materials, pointing, gesturing, or vocalizing to convey her message or question.

> Leslie's communication is limited by her inability to articulate sounds due to oral motor involvement resulting from her cerebral palsy. She is unable to articulate words to communicate her wants, needs, and emotional states without assistance from a voice generating system. She has attempted sign language in the past, but limited success was seen due to the extent of limitations by her right hand.

Functional level of oral, written and gestural expressive language capabilities, including oral motor speech status, and the communication functions of requesting, protesting, labeling and sharing information:

> Leslie's oral-motor limitations preclude verbal interactions despite nearly 13 years of speech therapy. She will use gestures but prefers to use her voice output device and facial expressions to communicate her ideas to others. She is a persistent and frequent communicator. She uses her device to share personal information, answer questions presented to her, and to state her physical and emotional needs and states.

Communicative interest:

> Leslie is a highly social individual. If she is comfortable, she will greet others with a smile and a wave. She appears consistently delighted to be involved in conversations with others. She demonstrates a strong desire to share information with others regarding her thoughts and ideas. Leslie works very hard, is willing to assist others, and persists in tasks even when they are difficult for her. Leslie shares confidentially that she wants to be challenged and learn new things.

Identification of a reliable and consistent motor response which can be used independently to communicate:

> Leslie is able to use her left hand to select desired areas/buttons on her communication device without difficulty.

<u>Assessment of present and future communication needs, including the types of communication needed, with whom, and in what environments</u> (e.g., to enhance conversation, and/or to write and signal emergency, basic care and related medical needs):

> Leslie currently uses her device to communicate with those in her school environment (e.g., including teachers, peers, and staff members). She enjoys interacting with others and will attempt to initiate communication in the community through facial expressions and use of her augmented system. In community based activities, Leslie requires prompting to use her device.

> It is anticipated that as Leslie continues to seek vocational opportunities and community involvement, she will need to express her thoughts, needs, and emotions through her device. Her device is also a key to expressing physical states (e.g., pain, discomfort) with others. Her device may allow her to describe symptoms to a physician before physical problems progress to dangerous levels. It would also allow Leslie to identify or request modifications to her ankle orthosis or hand splints as needed.

> It is also anticipated that one day Leslie may choose to move to a group home or supported living setting. In this environment, it is expected that Leslie would need her device to address her physical and emotional states and needs.

Sample Assessment Report 1, *continued*

<u>Features needed in client communication system, as applicable:</u>

Type and number of messages, vocabulary size, coding system, symbol sets, message retrieval:

> A number of communication systems have been used on a trial basis with Leslie in the school setting since her previous communication system (original Dynavox) failed and was deemed too old to be repaired by the manufacturer. Given the information gleaned from many trials, it appears that the best device to meet Leslie's current and future needs would be defined by the following features:
>
> > Dynamic touch screen with adjustable location size
> >
> > Voice output capabilities
> >
> > Ability to pair pictures with words on a location
> >
> > Programmable by phrase or single word
> >
> > Digitized or synthesized speech (DEC talk or better)
> >
> > Virtually unlimited number of messages to be stored
> >
> > Onscreen access capability to control device parameters (e.g., volume, display)

Size, layout, system memory, optical indicators, auditory prompts, rate enhancement, programmability, computer compatibility:

> Leslie benefits from a dynamic touch screen display. Individual characters on the layout can be as small as 5/8 inch, but the static screen concept of generating through categories (as in Minspeak) proved too difficult for Leslie to master on a trial with the Delta Talker.

Type of input method (e.g., switches, mouth stick, head pointer, alternative keyboard, and direct selection, scanning, encoding):

> Leslie can use direct selection to select a desired location on her device to a size as small as 5/8 of an inch.

Type of output (e.g., speech, print, LCD, braille):

> Leslie prefers synthesized voice output for its consistency.

Mounting and portability:

> Leslie's device needs to be lightweight (preferably 3 pounds or less) to allow her to carry it independently without significantly affecting her ability to ambulate safely from one place to another. A supportive protective casing and durability are important features for Leslie in the event her device would be dropped.

Extent of training required to use the system and availability of training and technical assistance for its use:

> Leslie is familiar with using augmentative devices as she has used them for a number of years. Support for implementation and technical assistance is available currently through her teachers and speech-language pathologist in the school setting as well as the augmentative communication team. Leslie will continue to need support to add new messages to her device to meet unique needs over time. Her family members or other support staff can be trained to assist her in these tasks.

Availability of customer service by manufacturer or supplier:

> Both companies of devices being considered offer technical support via telephone and a one-year warranty included in the cost of the device.

Availability of trial rental period and statement regarding whether rental fees can be applied towards purchase price:

> With the Portable Impact product, a rental period is available for $60 per week for up to a four-week period plus $40 shipping fee. Within 90 days, this rental fee can be applied toward the purchase of the device. The rental fee for the Dynamyte from Dynavox systems is $75 per week for a maximum of 3 weeks with no shipping fees. Again, the rental fees paid can be applied toward the purchase of the device.

Other considerations:

> Leslie's device will require programming. If a Dynamyte is selected, her current vocabulary can be downloaded into her new device. If a Portable Impact is selected, her current vocabulary will need to be redesigned to adapt to that device. It would be imperative that picture symbols be available on whichever device is provided. That technological support for either option is available from the assistive technology team at BASSC and her school speech-language pathologist.

> Continued speech therapy will be provided for Leslie during her school years through the school system. Therapists who may not be familiar with her device will receive in-service training to understand the care and programming of this device as well as basic troubleshooting. This inservice is also available through the special education cooperative here at no cost to Leslie or her family. Continued technical support for appropriate intervention and vocabulary additions to her device is also available from BASSC.

<u>Summary of intervention options, to include:</u>

- <u>Description of the systems tried by client during or prior to the assessment and success in terms of actual ability, motivation, independence, and improvement in communication effectiveness:</u>

> Over the course of the past two years, Leslie has used a Dynavox 2C, DeltaTalker, Chat Box, and Dynamyte. Of these four, the most successful was the Dynamyte because of its portability and toughness as well as the dynamic screen. The dynamic screen allows the vocabulary to be arranged by categories with changing pictures to represent messages she may wish to share. The changing screen allows her increased vocabulary size to meet her communication needs without requiring excessive cognitive load as in the Minspeak system (DeltaTalker). Another system under consideration for Leslie is the dynamic screen device called Portable Impact. It is designed to be comparable to the Dynamyte in size and weight, and uses Boardmaker pictures as compared to Dynasyms. The two systems are outlined in side by side comparisons in the next section.

- <u>The advantages, disadvantages, cost, and availability of training/customer service, for the two or three most appropriate communication systems for the client as determined through the assessment, specifying available features and client needs for each:</u>

> The two options that appear most appropriate for Leslie are the Table Model from Portable Impact (Enkidu Research, Inc.) or the Dynamyte from Dynavox systems. Both products meet the specifications listed above. Both have technical support available by telephone. Prices and specifications for these two devices compare as follows:

Portable Impact Tablet Model	Dynamyte
Weight: 2 lbs.	Weight: 3.2 lbs.
Size: 8.9" x 6.5" x 1.3"	Size: 8" x 7" x 2"
7.75" diagonal screen 640x480 resolution	6.5" diagonal, active matrix color LCD with 640x480 resolution
DEC Talk software	DEC Talk software
32MB expanded memory card	16MB memory card
Avg. Battery life: 6-8 hours	Avg. Battery life: 5 hours continuous (rechargeable)
Price: $3900 device, case, external speaker,	$6395 device,
expanded memory card, and	$50 carrying case
editing software	$60 back-up software

- <u>Documentation of client trial and success, including ability, motivation, independence, and improvement in communication effectiveness, in using one or more recommended communication systems, which may be accomplished prior to or during the assessment, or the rental cost for which may be requested through the prior approval process following the assessment:</u>

  Leslie has successfully used a Dynamyte in her school environment during the past year. She has demonstrated good ability to access the device and an ever-increasing repertoire of skills and abilities in interacting with peers and adults using her device. She is noted to use the device in class to answer questions, to make conversation with peers, and to communicate with people in the community. Leslie is responsible with her device and is able to carry it independently given its size and weight.

- <u>Final recommendation of which system is most appropriate to meet the client's medical needs and why, to include documentation of a vendor's price quote, a copy of the warranty, the availability of maintenance, the shipping location, and a recommendation of at least one other system which would meet the client's medical needs.</u> (Department approval will be based on the most cost effective system that meets the individual's medical needs.)

  Leslie's team has procured a rental period for the Portable Impact device for Leslie's use to determine if it will adequately meet her needs. This rental period is scheduled for April 20-May 6, 2002. Barring any unforseen problems, the Portable Impact device will be the recommendation of the team for Leslie's device.

(Attach additional pages if necessary)

Required Attachments:

1. Prescription and Certification of Medical Necessity (including medical history information) (See Appendix M.)
2. Individual Treatment and Implementation Plan (attached)
3. Literature on Recommended Equipment (none included)

Signature of Preparer: *Daisy Page*

Address: 23 Flower Lane

St. Louis, MO 55555

Phone: 555-555-2300

Individual Treatment and Implementation Plan for Leslie Montgomery

Action	Responsible Party	Completion Date
Receive augmentative device	Augmentative communication team at BASSC	When approved
Examine device to ensure all needed parts are present	Augmentative communication team at BASSC	Within 2 days of receipt of device
Reinstate or build the vocabulary currently in her device to her new device	Augmentative team/School SLP	Within 10 days of receipt of device
Attend training on care of device	Provided by BASSC aug. comm. team for family, teachers, and support staff	Within 3 weeks of receipt of device
Implement the device in the classroom and community setting	Teachers/support staff	Within one week of training on care and use
Initiate the use of the device in the home environment and other social settings	Mother, sister	Within one week of training on care
Continue to add vocabulary and foster language growth through the device	SLP, aug. comm. team, teacher, parent, sister	Beginning after training on care and use—ongoing
Ongoing support for family and staff in use, care, maintenance, troubleshooting, and implementation.	Available through BASSC	Until age 21

Attachment 2

Augmentative Communication Evaluation

Student: Nancy Bewell   Date of Birth: 4-28-92

Parent: Robert/Felicia Bewell   Home District: Rocky Point
         342 Stonybrook
         Wainsworth, IL 55555   Attends: Developmental Center

Date of Evaluation: June 2, 2002

➤Reason for Referral

Nancy was referred for an augmentative communication evaluation as part of her triennial reevaluation. She is nonverbal.

➤Relevant Background Information

Nancy has a medical diagnosis of Trisomy 18. She also has Miltral valve dysplagia and patent ductus, small ear canals, and poor muscle tone. Previous testing results indicate she functions in the severe to profound range of mental impairment. Nancy is not ambulatory and does not verbalize. She is reliant on others for her personal care.

➤Evaluation Results

Nancy was seen for evaluation on June 2, 1999 in her classroom at the Developmental Center. Nancy received 0-3 services through Early Intervention and has attended the Developmental Center since that time. Her current teacher is Mr. Michael Beasley. Mr. Beasley and his aides were present in the room during this evaluation.

Initially, Nancy was observed working one-on-one with an aide at the table. She appeared to enjoy running her right hand through a series of string pellets on a toy presented to her. She appeared to listen to a book being read by the aide but did not look at the book or demonstrate joint attention to that task. Her caregiver reports that she likes things that are soft but not fuzzy.

Nancy was next involved in a group activity at the table. With four students present, she sat with an aide who assisted her hand-over-hand to activate a rocker switch when it was presented to her to answer questions. No independent initiation was noted during those tasks. Nancy was noted to rub her head on the back of her chair and attempt to rub her head with her left hand. She was wearing a hat which the staff explained helped to keep her from rubbing her hair completely off. She was noted to vocally protest when her hand was moved to touch a certain picture during the group time activity. She was also noted to anticipate negative input and worked to avoid it by physically moving her head or face away from the undesirable stimulus.

Later, Nancy was placed on the floor for free time. During this time the examiners were able to interact and attempt to determine some of her preferences and any signaling behavior that she presently demonstrates. When she was placed on the floor, she immediately rolled onto her stomach and began to rub the front of her head on the mat vigorously back and forth. When the examiner began to roll a ball with medium pressure up and down her spine, she immediately stopped the head turning and her body was noted to relax at the shoulders. When the examiner stopped rolling the ball, Nancy waited a few seconds and then began to move her head back and forth again. When the ball rolling was resumed, Nancy again stopped the head movement and relaxed. The next time the ball rolling was stopped, Nancy simply turned her head to the other side one time and waited for the event to resume. After the third round, Nancy did not indicate a desire to continue the rolling, so the activity was discontinued.

Next, Nancy was presented with a musical toy behind her head. She was noted to roll to one side to listen and began to request the music with a vocalization. She was noted to request more through this method for the remainder of the free play session.

➢**Summary and Recommendations**

Nancy is a child with significant physical and mental challenges who indicates a desire to signal to those in her environment to effect change and gain certain reinforcers. Therefore, it would be important that a signal system be established to allow her more control over her environment and more participation in choosing when and how her needs are met.

Nancy demonstrates a need for sensory input as evidenced by her frequent head rubbing (both with her hand and against her chair and the mat). Her teacher also states that Nancy enjoys rocking, which may assist in meeting her need for vestibular input. A systematic approach for determining her desires could be achieved by completing a variety of sensory exercises with Nancy to determine desirable inputs. Then, a signal/object system could be established to assist her in communicating her needs or wants for those inputs throughout the day. A program such as *Every Move Counts* (Korsten et al., available from Therapy Skill Builders, 800-211-8378) could serve as the basis for such an evaluation.

As Nancy's signaling skills improve, consider the use of an object choice board where she can signal her choice by giving the requested item to a communication partner to gain the desired reinforcer. This type of activity would best be achieved by implementation in the classroom where numerous opportunities could be presented throughout the day.

It was a pleasure to work with Nancy. If we can be of further assistance, please do not hesitate to contact us.

Jenny Speakwell
Jenny Speakwell, MS, CCC-SLP
Speech-Language Pathologist

Melia Bestfit
Melia Bestfit, MPH, OTR/L
Assistive Technologist

Augmentative Communication Evaluation

Student: Jennifer Lindwell

Date of Birth: 12-13-85

Parent: Mike/Linda Lindwell
23 Michaels Drive
Sailorsville, NE 55555

Resident District: Parkland HS

Attends: Parkland High School

Date of Evaluation: April 3, 2002

Chronological Age: 16 years, 4 months

➤**Reason for Referral**

Jennifer was referred by her school IEP team to determine appropriate methods to augment her verbal communication. She has received speech therapy throughout her school years but continues to have limited functional speech.

➤**Relevant Background Information**

Jennifer has a diagnosis of congenital myopathy, Mobius syndrome, with bilateral facial paralysis, respiratory distress syndrome, and tracheomalacia. She has a permanent tracheostomy with a speaking valve and a gastronomy tube for feeding. She is able to suction herself but often needs reminders to do so.

Jennifer is non-ambulatory and moves about her environment via a hydraulic wheelchair that she controls with a joystick. She has also undergone two spinal fusion surgeries with a posterior fusion from C8-sacrum and an anterior fusion above the C8 level.

Jennifer had a previous augmentative communication evaluation in 1991. At that time, Jennifer demonstrated functional communication at the early symbolic level. The recommendation was made for a Touch Talker system that was purchased for her use. The symbol system used was IEP+ (Interaction, Education and Play Plus). This system was difficult for Jennifer to use due to the complex nature and the heavy memory load it required. By 1994, it was abandoned and emphasis returned to promoting verbal speech and sign language.

➤**Current Status**

At a recent IEP meeting, Jennifer's mother shared that Jennifer was considered for some oral surgeries to address her extremely high arched palate and her excess mandibular bone length. The consulting physician felt that he could correct these difficulties through surgically removing part of each mandible and reconstructing the palatal arch. However, it was discussed that Jennifer's saliva would then pool in the back of her throat, rather than the front, and with an absent swallow reflex, she would be more at risk for aspiration than she is currently. Jennifer's mother has decided not to proceed with that surgery but may consider a "retainer like" appliance. It would hook onto Jennifer's teeth and may allow her tongue to make contact with her palate for improved intelligibility in her speech.

Jennifer's IEP dated 4/21/99 indicates that she does math calculations with touch point aids, and is able to tell time to the half hour. She is reading at about the 2.0 grade level. She communicates with short, verbal phrases using approximated speech sounds. She has decreased muscular strength for speech production so some nonverbal signs are used to facilitate functional communication.

Further discussion at the IEP meeting on October 12, 2001 centered on oral-motor skills and weaknesses that Jennifer possesses. Jennifer has worked with her current speech therapist for the past year on improving oral motor skills. In November, 2001, Jennifer underwent surgery to reduce the tracheostomy opening to attempt to improve her speech. She now demonstrates increased volume, thereby making it easier to hear her in a quiet room. However, it appears that the structural differences coupled with the low facial tone and muscle weakness will continue to impede her ability to speak with adequate articulation and breath support to be her sole communicative mode.

➤ Present Evaluation

Jennifer is currently enrolled in a self-contained classroom and is working on daily living and assistance skills in addition to functional academics. She has a personal care attendant with her to assist with her physical needs.

Jennifer responds to greetings and *yes/no* questions with verbal or gestural responses. She cannot swallow independently, but she is able to suction herself. At times she needs reminders to do so, especially when she is very interested in what she is doing. Expressively Jennifer is severely limited by her low tone and demonstrates word finding difficulties to which she often responds by shrugging her shoulders and giving up.

Jennifer's receptive language is well above her expressive language. During this evaluation she was noted to respond properly to requests, directives, and humorous situations. She was able to understand dual meanings of words and responded appropriately to materials presented. She is able to do some basic calculations in her head but preferred to use a calculator for ease.

➤ Trial Periods

A trial period was conducted with Prentke Romich's Vanguard at Jennifer's school in the conference room. She was immediately able to understand the touch screen concept when presented with the device. She was noted to access with her right fourth finger, then later began to use other digits to activate keys including her thumbs. A different method was later employed in which she touched the screen with the top of her nail. The feature of written words on the icons appeared to assist her tremendously in her ability to sequence icons to create appropriate sentences.

Once the basic single hit messages had been explained, the second level of the Unity software was introduced. This level of software involves the use of multiple meanings of pictures to determine the rationale for vocabulary storage strategies. Again, once the basics were explained, Jennifer began to freely roam around the device finding appropriate ways to explore and interact with the others in the room using the device. She was noted to scan the entire screen for messages she wanted to use, and was able to sequence single icons and phrases into longer messages to make sentences. Once an icon was introduced, Jennifer was able to remember the location of that item on the screen.

➤**Access/Mounting/Classroom Accessibility**

The Vanguard was attached to an adjustable desktop mount for the evaluation period. Jennifer was able to touch all areas on the screen and was noted to support her elbow on the table. When the device was held in front of her, as if it were mounted to her chair, she was able to reach all areas without elbow support. It should be noted that she could use her armrest for this support if necessary.

Jennifer does not transfer from her wheelchair while at school. She is able to raise and lower her seat to enable her to pull up to most surfaces. For tasks that require desktop use, Jennifer could access the Vanguard if it were mounted to a desktop mount as was provided during the evaluation. This would enable verbal responses other than gestures during activities that require her to use her hands. To enable communication while moving about, the Vanguard should have the capability to be mounted to Jennifer's wheelchair. This can be accomplished with a DaeSSey mount. The specifications are attached.

➤**Summary and Recommendations**

Jennifer is a 16-year, 4-month-old child with a diagnosis of congenital myopathy, Mobius syndrome who has limited verbal communication. She currently lacks a way to make her needs, wants, and feelings known in a variety of situations. She has previously used a communication device with limited success due to the heavy memory load that the device required. Current evaluation results indicate that receptive language skills are significantly better developed than her expressive language abilities based on her physical limitations. It is therefore recommended that a device be purchased for her that meets the following requirements.

- Uses pictures and written words to cue vocabulary locations
- Dynamic screen
- Vocabulary that can be customized
- Voice output
- Touch screen accessible with light touch
- Icons at least ¾ inch square in size
- Mountable on wheelchair
- Removable for desktop use
- Adequate battery charge for full day's use

The Source for AAC—Appendix G ·168·

Systems that would appear to initially meet these criteria include the Vanguard from Prentke Romich, and the Dynavox from Sentient Systems Technology. Other computer-based systems may also meet her needs (e.g., Chameleon, Axis, Pegasus), but they also include peripheral computer functions in their systems. It is felt that Jennifer would benefit most from a device that is totally dedicated to improving her communication as she can access computers in other locations.

Of the two systems considered, the Vanguard appears to be the system of choice. It requires less programming as it comes with the Unity Minspeak program loaded on it, giving a core vocabulary of 500 words and hundreds of extended words used less often for specific subjects or situations. It allows customized pages to be created that would be unique to certain environments or situations. Jennifer demonstrated spontaneity using it and appeared enthusiastic about its content and ease of use.

Additionally, the Vanguard system allows visual recognition of icon meanings by supplying the written message under the picture. The icon prediction system will enhance Jennifer's speed and accuracy of her communication capabilities.

Support and training for any device or system purchased for Jennifer is available through the Central Augmentative Communication Support Team. Additional support may be available from the vendor, depending on the system purchased.

It was a pleasure to work with Jennifer and her support staff. If you have any questions or concerns, please do not hesitate to contact us 555-5555.

Jenny Speakwell
Jenny Speakwell, MS, CCC-SLP
Speech-Language Pathologist

Melia Bestfit
Melia Bestfit, MPH, OTR/L
Assistive Technologist

Equipment List

Available from:

Prentke Romich Company
1022 Heyl Road
Wooster, OH 44691
1-800-262-1933

Vanguard (VG-EXBP)		$7,995
Serial Cable (WI-312)		$47
Case (CC-VG)		$150
	Shipping:	$29

Includes Unity vocabulary software, two batteries for 8 hours of operating time, battery charger, memory transfer interface for IBM, infrared capabilities, manual and instructional books. The serial cable is used to transfer text directly to a computer.

The following mounting items are available directly from:

Daedalus Technologies
2491 Vauxhall Place
Richmond, BC V6V 1Z5
Canada

DaeSSy Desktop Mount (DM)		$265
DaeSSy Rigid Mount for wheelchair for Vanguard (DRM1)		$510
Identify X = 26", Y = 20" for tubing		
To be mounted on wheelchair rectangular tubing ¾" X 1.5		$20
	Shipping:	$20
	Total	$9,036

_____
              date

To Whom It May Concern:

Ashley is a patient of mine with a diagnosis of cerebral palsy. Despite years of intervention and speech therapy, Ashley has been unable to develop clear, intelligible speech. At age eight, the decision was made to use an augmentative communication device (original Dynavox) to assist her in communicating her wants, needs, and emotional states.

At this time, her device has broken and is in need of replacement. Ashley has recently participated in an extensive evaluation including a number of trial periods with augmentative communication devices. I concur with the findings of this evaluation team and have attached a prescription for a Dynamyte device and necessary accessories. I feel a voice prosthesis is the only option available to Ashley to express her needs, share information, and gain independence.

Please call me at _____ if you have questions or require further information.

Sincerely,

_Jerome Fixit, M.D._____

To Whom It May Concern:

We have been working with Susie Jones, an eight-year-old student, for the past year in attempting to determine the best augmentative communication device for her use. We are currently in a one-month trial period with a DeltaTalker. We would like to share what we have seen during the first two weeks of this experience.

Susie has demonstrated independent initiation of communication using her device in therapy sessions, as well as in unstructured social situations with her peers. She has demonstrated the ability to remember icon sequence locations without cues. She has used her device to answer questions posed to her by others. She has used her device to state her preferences and feelings.

From a fine motor perspective, Susie has demonstrated improved fine motor planning for use of the device and is now able to use all five digits of her left hand to access individual keys to produce her messages. She has demonstrated excellent accuracy in selecting her icons. At times, when positioning of the device has been difficult due to her current wheelchair situation, Susie has demonstrated persistence in using the device to get her message across.

One current concern is that Susie is currently being fitted for a new wheelchair. The request was sent to the vendor in December, and Susie and her family are awaiting word on approval and delivery of the chair. When that chair arrives, it would be the time to determine the appropriate chair mount as specific measurements of chair frame and tube height are necessary. It is recommended that during the interim, a desk mount be used so that she has a more upright positioning for the device, which allows her to activate the keys with her best movements. This desk mount would continue to be used for tabletop activities after the wheelchair arrives.

Technically, Susie demonstrates independence in following icon prediction indicators, clearing the message screen after each production, and understanding how to repeat a phrase when a conversational partner requests a repetition. Once taught an icon sequence, Susie demonstrates excellent memory skills. She understands conceptually the location of the Minspeak categories and their associations. She uses a variety of problem solving strategies to find the correct sequence when she is independently attempting a new or novel utterance. Each day that she uses the device, she demonstrates improved confidence in her abilities.

This device has only been with Susie for two weeks, but she is already well on her way to becoming a proficient user of this technology. Her initiation of communication, her excellent memory for locations of stored messages, and her persistence in finding a message and "getting it right" are all excellent indicators that Susie will use such a device to its full potential. It is anticipated that such a device will remove the barriers to Susie's ability to communicate her wants, needs, and emotions.

This trial has proved the need that can be filled and the rewards achieved for Susie with a dedicated communication device. Susie demonstrates improved communication, initiation, self-confidence, and independence in communicating her wants and needs using the device. Such a system will make a major impact on her ability to live independently and share with others her wants, needs, and emotional states. We strongly support the acquisition of this device for Susie.

Linda Smith
_____
Linda Smith, MS, CCC-SLP
Speech-Language Pathologist

Mary Parks
_____
Mary Parks, MPH, OTR/L
Assistive Technologist

Barb Johnson
_____
Barb Johnson, M.Ed
Teacher

References

American Psychiatric Association. 1994. *Diagnostic and statistical manual of mental disorders.* 4th ed. Washington, D.C.: American Psychiatric Association.

American Speech-Language-Hearing Association. l991. Report: Augmentative and alternative communication. *ASHA*, 33 (Suppl.5): 9-12.

Baker, B. 1982. Minspeak: A semantic compaction system that makes self-expression easier for communicatively disabled individuals. *Byte*, 7, 186-202.

Beukelman, D. R. & Mirenda, P. 1998. *Augmentative and alternative communication: Management of severe communication disorders in children and adults.* 2nd ed. Baltimore: Paul H. Brookes Publishing Co.

Blackstone, S, ed. 1986. *Augmentative communication: An introduction.* Rockville, MD: American Speech-Language-Hearing Association.

Blischak, D. M. & Wasson, C. A. l997. Sensory impairments. In *Augmentative and alternative communication: A handbook of principles and practices*, edited by L. L. Lloyd, D. R. Fuller & H. H. Arvidson, 254-279. Boston: Allyn and Bacon.

Bondy, A. S. 1996. *The pyramid approach to education.* Newark, Delaware: Pyramid Educational Consultants, Inc.

Bzoch, K. & League, R. 1972. *Receptive-expressive emergent language scale.* Baltimore: University Park Press.

Carlson, F. 1985. *Picsyms categorical dictionary.* Lawrence, KS: Baggeboda Press.

Carr, E. G., Levin, L., McConnachie, G., Carlson, J., Kemp, D. C., & Smith, C. E. l994. *Communication-based intervention for problem behavior: A user's guide for producing positive change.* Baltimore: Paul H. Brookes Publishing Co.

Carrow-Woolfolk, E. 1999. *Test for auditory comprehension & language—third edition* (TACL-3) Austin: Pro-Ed, Inc.

DeBoer, A. 1995. *Working together: The art of consulting and communicating.* Longmont, CO: Sopris West.

Dettmer, P., Dyck, N., & Thurston, L. P. 1999. *Consultation, collaboration, and teamwork for students with special needs.* Boston: Allyn and Bacon.

Dunn, L. & Dunn, L. 1997. *Peabody picture vocabulary test—third edition* (PPVT-III) Circle Pines, MN: American Guidance Service.

Elder, P. S., & Goosens, C. 1996. *Engineering training environments for interactive augmentative communication: Strategies for adolescents and adults who are moderately/severely developmentally delayed.* 2nd ed. Birmingham, AL: Southeast Augmentative Communication.

Finnerty, J., & Quill, K. 1991. *The communication analyzer.* Lexington, MA: Educational Software Research.

Frost, L. & Bondy, A. 1994. *The picture exchange communication system (PECS) training manual.* Cherry Hill, NJ: Pyramid Educational Consultants, Inc.

Gardner, M. F. 2000. *Receptive one-word picture vocabulary test* (ROWPVT). Novato, CA: Academic Therapy Publications.

Glennen, S. L. & DeCoste, D. C. 1997. *Handbook of augmentative and alternative communication.* San Diego: Singular Publishing Group, Inc.

Goosens, C. 1989. Aided communication before assessment: A case study of a child with cerebral palsy. *Augmentative and Alternative Communication*, 5, 14-26.

Goosens, C., Crain, S., & Elder, P. 1992. *Engineering the preschool environment for interactive, symbolic communication: An emphasis on the developmental period 18 months to five years.* Birmingham, AL: Southeast Augmentative Communication Conference, Clinician Series.

Higginbotham, D. J. 2001. Introduction: Research on utterance-based communication. *Special division 12 augmentative and alternative communication.* Rockville, MD: American Speech-Language-Hearing Association.

Hourcade, J. J., Parette, H. P., & Huer, M. B. 2002. Family and cultural alert: Considerations in assistive technology assessment. *Annual Editions Education Exceptional Children*, 14, 82-86.

Janzen, J. E. 1996. *Understanding the nature of autism: A practical guide.* San Antonio: Therapy Skill Builders.

Johnson, R. 1994. *The picture communication symbols combination.* Solana Beach, CA: Mayer-Johnson Co.

King, T. 1999. *Assistive technology: Essential human factors.* Boston: Allyn and Bacon.

Korsten, J. E., Dunn, D. K., Foss, T. V., & Francke, M. K. 1993. *Every move counts: Sensory-based communication techniques.* Overland Park, KS: Responsive Management, Inc.

Kumin, L. 1994. *Communication skills in children with down syndrome: A guide for parents.* Rockville, MD: Woodbine House.

Kumin, L. 2001. *Classroom language skills for children with down syndrome: A guide for parents and teachers.* Bethesda, Maryland: Woodbine House.

Linder, T. 1990. *Transdisciplinary play-based assessment: A functional approach to working with young children.* Baltimore: Paul H. Brookes Publishing Co.

Lloyd, L. L., Fuller, D. R., & Arvidson, H. H. 1997. *Augmentative and alternative communication: A handbook of principles and practices.* Boston: Allyn and Bacon.

National Joint Committee for the Communication Needs of Persons with Severe Disabilities. 1992. Guidelines for meeting the communication needs of persons with severe disabilities. *ASHA*, 34 (Suppl. 7): 2-3.

Paul, R. 2001. *Language disorders from infancy through adolescence: Assessment and intervention.* 2nd ed. St. Louis: Mosby, Inc.

Public Law 94-142. 1975. *Education for all handicapped children act of 1975.* Washington, D.C.: U.S. Congress.

Public Law 105-17. 1977. *Individuals with disabilities education act reauthorization amendments of 1997.* Washington, D.C: U.S. Congress.

Public Law 100-407. 1988. *Technology-related assistance act of 1988.* Washington, D.C.: U.S. Congress.

Public Law 101-336. 1990. *Americans with disabilities act of 1990.* Washington, D.C.: U.S. Congress.

Quill, K. (ed.). 1995. *Teaching children with autism: Strategies to enhance communication and socialization.* Albany, NY: Delmar Publishers.

Richard, G. J. & Hoge, D. R. 1999. *The Source for Syndromes.* East Moline, IL: LinguiSystems, Inc.

Rossetti, L. 1990. *The Rossetti infant-toddler language scale.* East Moline, IL: LinguiSystems, Inc.

Rouse, C. & Katera. 2000. *Ideas and materials to take picture communication systems beyond choice making.* Las Vegas, NV: Creative Communication Solutions.

Silverman, F. S. 1989. *Communication for the speechless.* 2nd ed. Englewood Cliffs, NJ: Prentice-Hall, Inc.

Snell, M.E. & Janney, R. 2000. *Collaborative teaming: Teacher's guides to inclusive practices.* Baltimore: Paul H. Brookes Publishing Co., Inc.

Van Dijk, J. 1986. An educational curriculum for deaf-blind multiply handicapped persons. In *Sensory impairments in mentally retarded people*, edited by D. Ellis, 375-382. San Diego: College-Hill Press.

Woodruff, G., & McGonigel, M. J. 1988. Early intervention team approaches: The transdisciplinary model. In *Early Childhood Special Education: Birth to Three*, edited by J. B. Jordan, J. J. Gallagher, P. L. Hutinger & M. B. Karnes, 163-182. Reston, VA: Council for Exceptional Children and the Division for Early Childhood.

Yorkston, K. M. & Karlan, G. R. 1986. Assessment procedures. In *Augmentative communication: An introduction*, edited by S. Blackstone, 163-196. Rockville, MD: American Speech-Language-Hearing Association.

Zabala, J. S. *Get SETT for successful inclusion and transition.* January 18, 2002 [Online]. *http://www.ldonline.org/ld_indepth/technology/zabalaSETT1.html*

Zangari, C., Lloyd, L. L., & Vicker, B. 1994. Augmentative and alternative communication: An historic perspective. *Augmentative and Alternative Communication*, 10:27-59.

Zimmerman, I. L., Steiner, V. G., & Pond, R. E. 1992. *Preschool language scale—third edition* (PLS-3). San Antonio: The Psychological Corporation.